Basic astro navigation

By the same author:
Basic Coastal Navigation
Start to Navigate

Basic astro navigation

Conrad Dixon

ADLARD COLES LIMITED
GRANADA PUBLISHING
London Toronto Sydney New York

Published by Granada Publishing in
Adlard Coles Limited, 1979
First published 1968
Reprinted 1973, 1975
Reprinted with amendments 1976
Reprinted 1979

Granada Publishing Limited
Frogmore, St Albans, Herts AL2 2NF
and
3 Upper James Street, London W1R 4BP
1221 Avenue of the Americas, New York, NY 10020 USA
117 York Street, Sydney, NSW 2000, Australia
100 Skyway Avenue, Toronto, Ontario, Canada M9W 3A6
Trio City, Coventry Street, Johannesburg 2001, South Africa
CML Centre, Queen & Wyndham, Auckland 1, New Zealand

ISBN 0 229 98579 3

Printed in Great Britain by
Fletcher & Son Ltd, Norwich

Sincere thanks are due to Thomas Reed Publications Limited, whose *Reed's Nautical Almanac* is used throughout, and to Captain O. M. Watts for his sound practical advice and assistance. I am indebted to the cartoonist 'Ward' and Associated Newspapers Limited, to the Controller of H.M. Stationery Office and the Hydrographer of the Navy for permission to reproduce illustrations. The cover illustration is reproduced by courtesy of Henry Browne and Sons Ltd.

Contents

Preface

This book has three aims: to present astro navigation in the simplest possible terms, to sandwich lumps of theory between slices of practice to make them more digestible, and to use one work of reference for all purposes. The idea is that a week's easy reading will give a good grasp of the elements involved in finding latitude and longitude from observations of the sun and stars, and the ability to plot the position of a yacht accurately by day and by night. The work is tailored to the man or woman who has some experience of coastal cruising and who now wants to make off-shore passages of between 150 and 500 miles prior to having a crack at an ocean crossing. It does not pretend to explain formulae or ratios, spherical triangles or equations: it was written for the amateur navigator who wants to know how it works – not why it works – and to give him confidence to explore our last frontier, the open sea, where the wind is king.

1 *Looking at the world*

'South till the butter melts – then West!'
Traditional sailing instructions given to
masters of small vessels trading to the West Indies.

Every day of the year small yachts put out from one port or another to cross the wide seas between the countries and continents of the world. These little ships and their amateur crews generally leave port with hardly any fuss and even less publicity. Safe arrivals are occasionally reported in the newspapers: more often than not only friends and relatives know from a series of colourful postcards that the various stages of the voyage have been completed. The people who crew these little ships are hardly ever tough young athletes at the peak of physical condition, or mathematical egg-heads with a natural genius for navigation. They are, most commonly, men and women living on that even plateau of life between thirty and sixty years of age who have put by enough money to finance a voyage, and acquired enough sense to turn away from the noisy, crowded life of our cities. They come in all sizes. They are fat and lean, robust and invalid, clean-shaven and bearded, cheerful and morose. None of them are rich; few have received any formal instruction in navigation, some are not even experienced seamen. Yet, they make landfalls, and good ones too. There are very few fatalities. From a statistical point of view they are almost as safe as regular airline passengers: certainly they are less at risk than the car driver dicing daily with death on inter-urban motorways. Once well off the land the navigational art becomes merely part of the overall problem of getting the boat

and crew to a chosen destination in safety, and with the
least possible delay. Astro navigation is not difficult.
It does not require wide theoretical knowledge of
geometry and trigonometry, the brain of an astrono-
mer or the neatness of a design draughtsman. Anyone
who can add, subtract, use a sextant and read a table
can navigate a small vessel to any charted spot on earth.

Learned men tell us that this planet on which we live

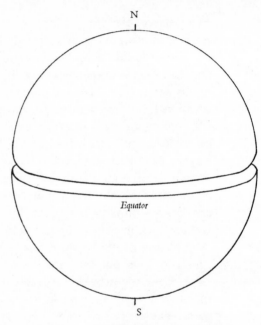

Figure 1

hangs in space like a huge orange; an orange somewhat
flattened at the top and bottom where polar ice covers
the sea. Small yachts don't make voyages to the North
and South Poles, so we can treat the earth as a perfect
sphere for our purposes. It's a large planet with a radius
of nearly 4,000 miles, and this great size gives us two
priceless advantages. One is that the surface area is so
great, and the curvature so gentle, that imaginary
curved lines on the surface may be considered as

straight lines provided you don't make them more than about thirty sea-miles long each time: the other is that chart-makers can reproduce small portions of the earth's skin in chart form with only a few simple adjustments. We are thereby able to translate curved tracks on a sphere into straight lines on flat charts.

Keep on thinking about the earth as an orange with the stalk joint, the North Pole, uppermost. Cut the orange horizontally through the centre and the line of the cut represents the Equator (see figure 1). It stands to reason that there has to be a starting point for

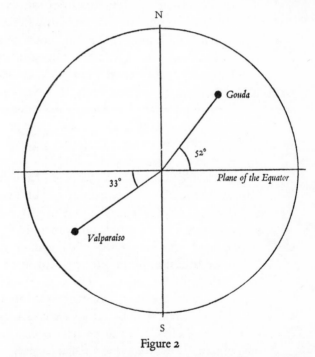

Figure 2

measuring geographical position on the surface of the earth, and the equator is the first imaginary line to give position. By starting at the equator we can say, first, that a place is either north or south of the equator. Next, we can say it is so far north, or so far south, of the

equator by relating it to the plane of the cut of the
equator. An imaginary line from the place to the centre
of the earth makes an angle with the plane of the
equator; that angle is the latitude of the place. Thus, in
figure 2 the pleasant Dutch inland port of Gouda is at
an angle of 52° to the plane of the equator, while the
busy town of Valparaiso is at an angle of 33° to the
plane of the equator. The latitude of Gouda may be
expressed as 52° N and that of Valparaiso as 33° s. This
knowledge of the exact angular distance from the
equator, or latitude, was of the greatest assistance to
navigators in previous centuries who were prone to
lose track of their reckoning through storms, damage
or faulty chronometers. A handbook in my possession
dating from 1846 contains a standard list of . . . 'The
Latitudes . . . of Remarkable Harbours, Islands, Shoals,
Capes, &c.' so that masters of vessels in this predica-
ment who were uncertain of their position could sail
north or south until they got to the right latitude, and
then turn east or west until they sighted the particular
feature they were looking for. Many yachtsmen with
crippled craft and lost instruments have done the same.
Voss† lost his only companion and his steering compass
during a voyage from Fiji to Australia, but by using his
quadrant to get latitude and the set of the ocean swell
to keep him on course made Sydney Harbour only
some fifteen minutes out in his calculations.

Back to the orange. The line of any cut passing
through the centre, whether vertical, horizontal or
diagonal, represents a Great Circle. Great circles are the
largest circles that can be drawn on the surface of a
sphere. They are always equal in size, and a line be-

† John Claus Voss. He made a number of interesting voyages,
and is best remembered for his trip around the world in a converted dug-out canoe named *Tilikum*. He died in great poverty in
1922, but his book, *The Venturesome Voyages of Captain Voss*, is one
of the great classic sea stories of all time.

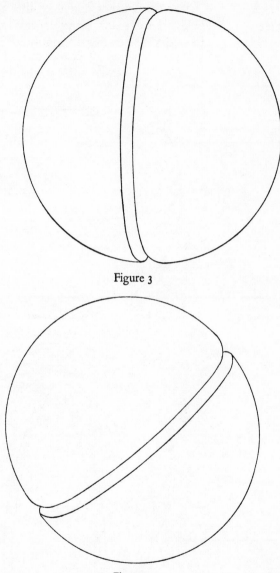

Figure 3

Figure 4

tween two points which follows the track of a great circle is the shortest distance between those points. Look at figures 3 and 4. Compare them with the equator in figure 1 and note that they are all great circles; the equator being a great circle with special properties of its own. Any other cut through the

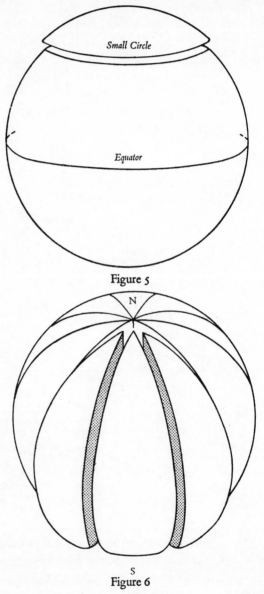

Figure 5

Figure 6

orange not passing through the centre is a Small Circle, as in figure 5. Where these small circles are parallel to the plane of the equator they are termed parallels of latitude.

This time cut your orange vertically through the centre a number of times, or split it up into segments with your fingers. The lines of the cuts or splits (see figure 6) correspond to Meridians, or lines of longitude. Once again, measurement must start somewhere, and an arbitrary line running from Pole to Pole through Greenwich is used as the starting point for working out

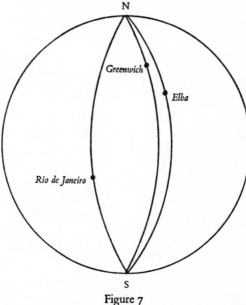

Figure 7

the position of a place east or west of that meridian. By standing at one of the poles and looking towards the equator you would be able to see a circle of land and sea spread before you with 360° of circumference. The meridian of Greenwich running towards the other pole is your starting point, and you work out the longitude of a place in terms of degrees of circumference east or west of Greenwich up to a maximum of 180° each way. Thus, in figure 7, the island of Elba is shown as being about 10° east of the Greenwich meridian, and Rio de Janeiro as being about 43° west of the Greenwich meridian. The longitude of Elba can be given as 10° East, and that of Rio de Janeiro as 43° West. One thing may puzzle you slightly. Round the back end of the world, in the Pacific, is a kind of navigational zip-fastener where 180° East and 180° West meet. Don't worry about it: by the time your boat has got that far you'll be able to add or subtract whole days from your reckoning with perfect confidence!

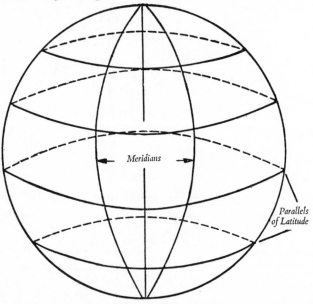

Figure 8

Before leaving this business of latitude and longitude think again about the imaginary corset of lines we have strapped about the long-suffering earth. Consider the equator as a particular great circle on which every point is at an angular distance of 90° from the poles. Think of the meridians as semi-great circles crossing the equator at right angles and running from pole to pole. Look at figure 8 and then at a solid globe to see what latitude and longitude look like in three dimensions. Get used to writing down the position of places correctly, thus ... 'Eddystone Rock Light House – position – 50° 11′ N, 4° 16′ W'. End by turning back to the solid globe and working out the latitude and longitude of places for yourself, checking the answers in an almanac or pilot book later.

2 *A taste of theory*

'You will never enjoy the world aright till the sea itself floweth in your veins, till you are clothed with the heavens and crowned with the stars.'
Traherne

The sun, the earth and the stars have a relationship of position that makes astro navigation a reality, and for thousands of years men have been looking up into the

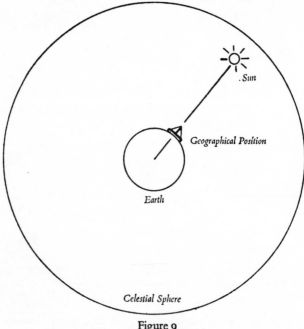

Figure 9

sky and noting the movements of the stars and planets. This mass of information is at our disposal; people with slide rules and enough formulae to fertilize a mathe-matician's garden have got the answers ready. All we

need for yacht navigation is a little background knowledge to understand the meaning of the phrases they
use, and enough grasp of the technique to enable us to
interpret the figures they supply.

The first concept to be understood is that of the

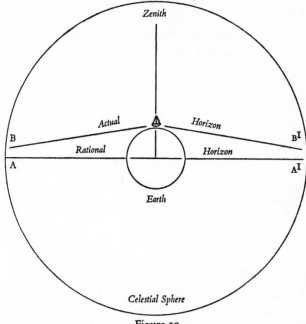

Figure 10

Geographical Position. Look at figure 9. Here, at a
certain point in time, a yacht is sailing along with
the sun directly overhead. Take away the yacht and
the geographical position remains: it is that point on the
skin of the earth through which passes an imaginary
line linking the sun and the centre of the earth. Put the
yacht back, and imagine yourself in the cockpit. The
sun is directly overhead, and is said to be at its Zenith.
Still think of yourself as being in the cockpit, and take
away the sun. That point directly above you is your
zenith.

Now look at figure 10. The yacht is still there and

the zenith point is marked. In this illustration you can also see the two horizons we use for position-finding. The horizon B–B¹ is what the man in the cockpit sees: it is also the horizon he uses to get angles from at the very start of his calculations. The horizon A–A¹ is the Rational Horizon passing through the centre of the earth; it is the horizon we must use to fix our relationship exactly with the stars and planets. Now move on to figure 11 which contains the key to a quick understanding of nautical astronomy.

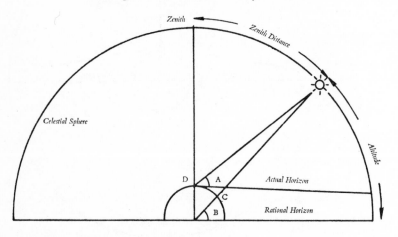

Angle A is the Observed Angle

Angle B is the True Angle

Position C is the Geographical Position

Position D is the Observer's Position

Figure 11

An observer in a yacht measures the angle between the sun and the actual horizon. He applies certain corrections to this angle and gets the true angle from the sun to the centre of the earth to the rational horizon. In figure 11 angle 'A' is the angle taken by the observer, and angle 'B' is the true angle at the centre of the earth. By subtracting angle 'B' (which is called the true altitude) from 90° we get the angle from the sun to the

centre of the earth to the zenith. The arc running along
the edge of the celestial sphere from the sun to the
zenith is called the Zenith Distance. Note that there is
a second arc running along the surface of the earth
from the observer's position at 'D' to the geographical

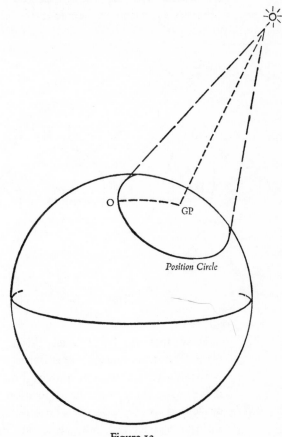

O

GP

Position Circle

Figure 12

position at 'C', and that this arc is called the Geographical Distance. Think about these two arcs. They
have a common angle at the centre of the earth, and
this common angle gives them the same number of
degrees and fractions of a degree on the arc. Now we

have angular distance on the surface of the earth because zenith distance (whose angle is known) equals
geographical distance (which we want). By expressing
degrees and minutes of arc in an equivalent number of
nautical miles we have obtained the number of miles
of distance on the surface of the earth from the
observer's position to the geographical position.

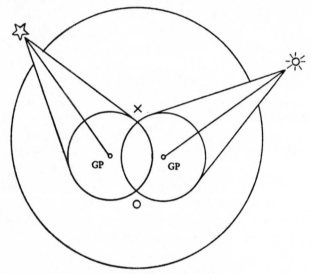

Figure 13

How does this help? Well, this figure in nautical
miles from the observer's position to the geographical
position gives us distance, but not direction. However,
if we make the geographical position the centre of a
circle and use the distance as a radius we can draw a
Position Circle, and somewhere on that circle will be
the observer in his yacht. Figure 12 shows a position
'cone' shining down on the surface of the earth: an
observer at any point on the position circle will be
getting the same angle of the sun's altitude. Take two
angles of two different bodies simultaneously, however, and you'll get two position circles intersecting,

as in figure 13. You'll probably know your dead reckoning position within a score of miles and can discard the second intersection at 'X' some hundreds of miles away. The one close to your dead reckoning position at 'O' is an astronomical 'fix' from two heavenly bodies. There is a deal of addition, subtraction and interpolation between taking the angle and drawing the position line in practice, but in a nutshell that is all there is to getting terrestial position lines from heavenly bodies.

Of course, you don't draw curved lines to get this fix. A small portion of the position circle is straightened and made to run at right angles to the radius of the position circle. Figure 14 shows such a straightened position line.

In case some readers still find it hard to grasp that distance on the surface of a sphere can be related to the angle at the centre of the sphere a look at figure 15 should resolve their doubts. We know that the radius of the earth is 3,596 nautical miles, and that by the magic of mathematics the arc from the pole to the equator is 5,400 miles long. The angle between pole and equator is 90° at the centre of the earth, and thus 1° at the centre of the earth projects 5,400 ÷ 90 = 60 nautical miles on the surface. Therefore, one degree of latitude equals 60 miles of latitude, and one minute of latitude equals one nautical mile.

Two other theoretical considerations can be dealt with briefly here before we move on to more practical matters. Because we are dealing with lines and angles taken from curved surfaces I have to introduce you to that nightmare of the sea-going apprentice – the Spherical Triangle. Professional seamen have to be able to calculate the various parts of these triangles from formulae: our solutions are found in tables. Figure 16 shows the earth with the equator and two meridians marked on it: in figure 17 I have lifted out the portion

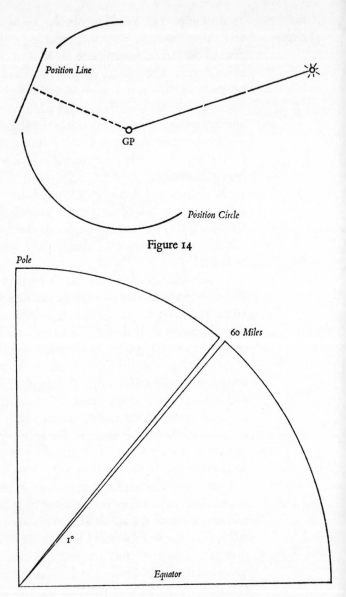

Figure 14

Figure 15

where the meridians and equator join – it is a spherical
triangle. These triangles are always composed of three

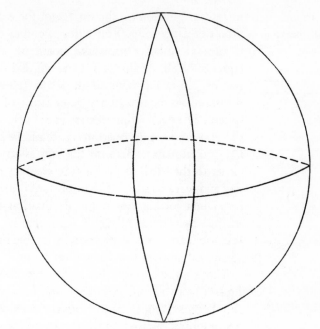

Figure 16

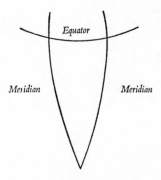

Figure 17

great circle arcs, and we shall meet them again later in
the book.

The last item concerns what is known as the Declination of a heavenly body. Think of declination as
another variety of latitude applying to planets and stars

27

instead of position on the surface of the earth and you won't be far wrong. You will remember that latitude is angular distance measured north or south of the equator. Well, declination is the angular distance of a star or planet north or south of the celestial equator measured on the imaginary outer fabric of the celestial sphere. The declination of stars varies very little during the year, and the declination figure can be found in the nautical almanac. Because the sun is so very much closer to the earth its declination changes from day to day and week to week. The important thing to remember when jotting down the declination figure is to include the prefix 'N' or 'S' for north or south. You will see later that the prefix tells us whether we have to add or subtract the declination figure.

That's quite enough theory for the moment. Study figures 11 to 14 and make sure you have the relationship between angles taken from the deck of a boat and geographical distance on the surface of the earth firmly fixed in your mind.

3 *The sextant*

Scene: the moorings at Cowes. A smartly-dressed
yachtsman is busy on deck; a small boy hails him from
the shore.

Small boy: 'Hey, mister!'

Yachtsman: (*impatiently*) 'What do you want?'

Small boy: 'Tell us where you're going, mister?'

Yachtsman: (*grandly*) 'Actually, I'm crossing over to
the mainland today'

Small boy: (*pretending to be very impressed*) 'Cor! Will
yer bring us back a parrot?'

The ocean navigator's complete do-it-yourself kit
consists of a watch or clock to give Greenwich Mean
Time accurately, a nautical almanac for the current
year, sundry tables, some charts or squared paper for
plotting, parallel rulers, dividers, pencils, a rubber and
an instrument for measuring angles. This last-named
instrument may be a sextant, but is not invariably so.
When I was first at sea the master used an octant: he
retired from the merchant service and I bought it for
a fiver. It had been made in 1871 and gave excellent
service until it was stolen from a laid-up yacht some
years back. A friend of mine, who is an airline pilot,
uses a quintant for sea navigation and swears by it. I
don't doubt that in the Indian Ocean some dhow skip-
per is getting good results from a backstaff or a Davis
quadrant, and that further east the Al-Kemal – a device
made of horn and string for taking the elevation of the
Pole Star – is still in use. The point is that all these
instruments measure angles: the sextant is merely the
one we are most familiar with, and the one most
commonly used for yacht navigation.

The name derives from the Latin *sextans* – the sixth part, and means that the size of the measuring arc is 60°, or a sixth part of a circle. Properly speaking, these instruments should be called mirror sextants because they are based on two very simple principles. The first is that the angle at which a ray of light strikes a polished surface is equal to the angle it makes as it reflects off the polished surface. For the technically minded it can be summed up in the phrase – 'the angle of incidence equals the angle of reflection'. Figure 18 illustrates this

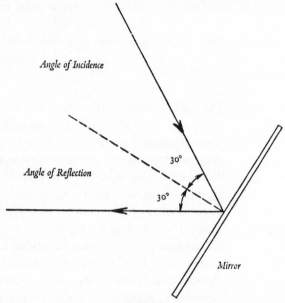

Figure 18

principle. The second is that through an optical quirk known as the principle of double reflection the 60° arc is marked to 120°, or a bit over, and we can measure angles well beyond the right angle. Figure 19 will tell you nearly all you'll want to know about the sextant: look at the illustration and follow the reasoning in the next paragraph.

The observer in figure 19 alters the setting of his

instrument so that the reflected image of the sun appears to touch the visible sea horizon. The rays of the real sun shine on to the index mirror and thence, at the same angle, on to the horizon mirror. From there they pass through the telescope to the eye of the observer. To get the image of the sun to touch the horizon

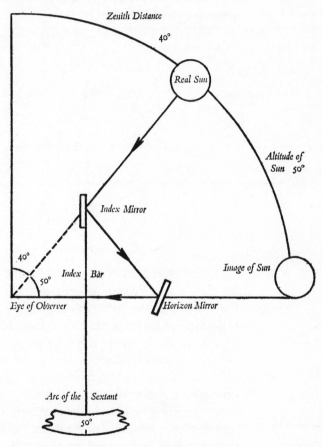

Figure 19

the observer has to adjust the index bar by pushing it forward, and this causes the end of the bar to move along the arc and eventually register on it the altitude of the sun. In this illustration the 50° angle of the sun above the horizon is faithfully reflected by a 50° reading on the arc of the sextant. I'll be going through the mechanics of taking sights in chapter five, but for the moment stow away in your mind the notion that by using two mirrors and a lever the angle between sun and horizon is transferred to the arc of the sextant where it is noted by the observer.

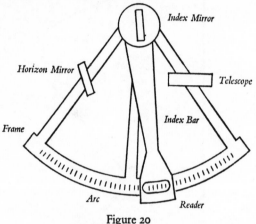

Figure 20

The principal parts of the sextant are shown in figure 20. Figure 21 depicts a modern micrometer sextant. The chief difference between old and new sextants lies in the type of reader at the end of the index bar where it joins the arc. In one of the older patterns you'll find a clamping screw and a fine adjustment screw on the end of the index bar, and the reading is made through a hinged magnifier directed at a vernier scale. (We'll come to reading verniers in the next chapter.) Another type also has a vernier, but the index bar is moved by a quick release button and an endless tangent screw. Fine adjustments are made by twirling the tangent screw at the forward end of the bar, and the advantage here is that the endless thread enables you to go on and on taking a series of sights without touching the quick

Figure 21.

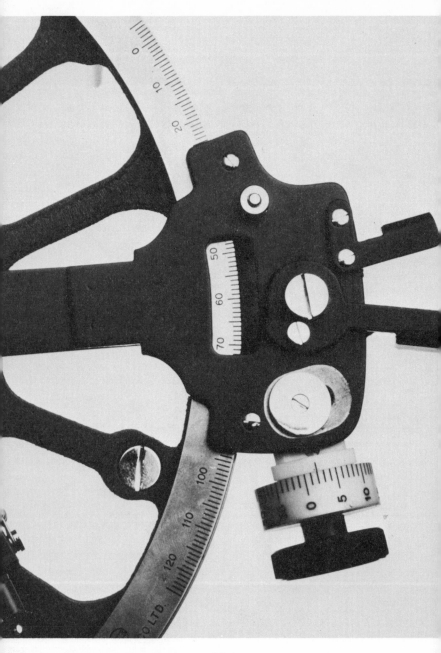

Figure 25a.

release button. Of course, up-to-date sextants have micrometer heads – as shown in figure 21. With these latest instruments all you have to do is to read the whole number of degrees straight off the arc and take the fractions of a degree off the micrometer by inspection. I don't suggest you worry too much about seconds, even though the instrument will give a reading to the nearest ten seconds: the nearest half minute will suffice.

Older sextants are usually provided with three tele-scopes to fit into the 'collar' attached to the frame of the instrument. If you should happen to start practising with your sextant by taking horizontal angles of shore marks you'll need to use the blank tube telescope with no lenses in it. The tube merely ensures that the line of sight is parallel to the plane of the instrument. For sun and star sights the bell-shaped (or star) telescope will be needed. This telescope will be the one most com-monly in use, and in some sextants it can be kept permanently shipped – even when the sextant is in its box. The third telescope is outwardly similar to the blank tube variety, but has lenses fitted. It is known as the inverting telescope because it inverts the images viewed through it. Try it by all means for star work: you'll probably find it is only suitable for use on the steady deck of a motor vessel. I always leave mine at home.

Take another look at figure 21. The mirrors can be covered by hinged shades when the sun is particularly bright. On my sextant the index mirror has three red and one green shades while the horizon mirror has two red shades and a green one. There is no rule for apply-ing these shades to cut down glare: you just have to experiment with the shades in turn until you get the best result for the conditions obtaining at the time.

Professional seamen buy their sextants from reput-able makers and ask for certificates of accuracy. This is reasonable enough, for a deck officer's reputation rests largely on his navigational expertise and he'll buy the best instrument he can afford. The yachtsman is not in the same category. He will be taking sights infrequently and in quite different conditions – usually in a small vessel low down on the water with a poor horizon. In such circumstances the best navigator in the world would be happy to get within, say, two miles of his correct position, and expensive instruments will not give appreciably better results. Yachtsmen should not be afraid of buying second-hand sextants despite Lecky's† warning that . . . 'The market is glutted with sextants MADE FOR SALE. Every pawnbroker's window in a seaport town is half full of them'. The yachtsman wants an instrument that can lie around for months in the lockers of a cruising boat and be used in conditions so bad that it has to be wrapped in a plastic bag to keep the spray off. The older type of vernier sextant with a cast-iron frame and brass fittings stands up to knocks and can be adjusted without recourse to instrument-makers. When buying secondhand don't be put off by dirt and verdigris – it can easily be cleaned off. If the sextant passes the various tests for error, has an undamaged arc, good shades and telescopes – buy it. You'll learn more about sextants by putting one in order than from all the books in the world, and you won't be afraid to take one out of the box in heavy weather for fear of damaging a valuable piece of equipment. One last word of warning. There are many bubble sextants on the market – mostly ex-RAF in origin. They can be used where there is a stable working platform, but are quite useless for yachts. Don't waste your money on them.

† Squire Thornton Stratford Lecky. The author of *Wrinkles in Practical Navigation.*

4   *Errors of the sextant*

'. . . the Quadrant was, in several respects, defective;
and, therefore, he wished that some steady hand could
be found to make a new one according to his direc-
tions, which Mr Rowley undertook, and performed in
such a masterly manner in all its parts, that not one
stroke or division is amiss, displaced or disproportioned
in the whole.'

From *A treatise containing the description and use of a new
and curious quadrant* . . . by Thomas Woodford, 1756.

Constant practice makes good navigators, and you'll
understand your sextant in fairly short order if you are
able to correct most of its errors yourself. Some of
what is said here is applicable to the buying of a
second-hand sextant, for you can run a quick check on
the working parts of the instrument by following these
simple rules.

The first error to look out for is what is known as
the error of perpendicularity. This alarming phrase
merely means that we have to test the instrument to
ensure that the index mirror is perpendicular (or at
right angles) to the plane of the sextant. Start by taking
the instrument out of its box and putting it on a table,
resting on its legs. Set the index bar to about 45° on the
arc and position yourself so that the index mirror is
nearest your eye, and the arc further away. Juggle
with the sextant until you can see the reflection of the
arc in the index mirror. As you look at the mirror
you'll see that the actual arc appears to join the reflected
arc at the right-hand side of the mirror. If the two arcs
make a continuous line you've got nothing to worry
about; there is no error of perpendicularity. If the arc

and reflected arc don't make a gentle continuing curve some error exists, and you've got to correct it by loosening or tightening the adjustment screw at the back of the index mirror. Remember that gently does it, and always start by slackening the screw at first: otherwise you'll put an undue strain on the backing of the mirror, and may even crack the glass. The adjustment should be done with an electrical screwdriver or a sail needle – depending on the type of adjustment screw, and you have to keep your eye on the mirror throughout the operation so that you'll know when the lines meet and the mirror is again perpendicular. Figure 22 shows what you should see when there is no error of perpendicularity.

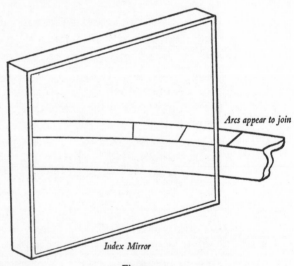

Arcs appear to join

Index Mirror

Figure 22

The second error is called side error; it is caused by the horizon mirror not being perpendicular to the plane of the sextant. To find side error you have to ship the star telescope, set the index bar to a zero reading on the arc and focus on a bright star, or the sun. Make fine adjustments so that the superimposed images cross each other. If they exactly cover each other at the moment of transit there is no side error, but if you see the star images side by side (as in the first part of figure 23), or with the suns out of line (as in the

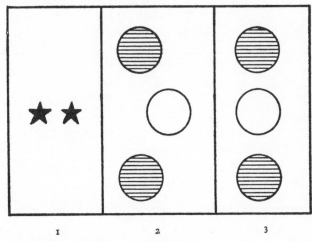

I   2   3

Figure 23

second part of the illustration), you've got side error.

On the back of the horizon mirror you'll find two screws. The outer one – the one distant from the frame – should be used to correct side error. By adjusting it a little at a time, and looking at the star, or the sun, between each adjustment it should be possible to get the two images to cover each other exactly and eliminate side error. With a bright star you should get a single image: with the sun the reflected images should appear directly over and under the real thing as in the third part of figure 23.

The third error is the most common, and is called index error. It is caused by the index and horizon mirrors not being exactly parallel to each other when the index bar is set to zero. It is found in almost the same way as side error by setting the index bar to zero on the arc, holding the sextant vertically, and looking at the horizon through the telescope. If, as in figure 24(1), you see a break in the line of the horizon the instrument has index error.

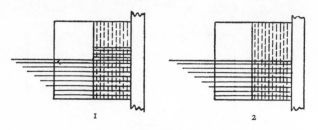

Figure 24

Index error is adjusted by means of the inner screw at the back of the horizon mirror – the one nearest the frame of the instrument. By gentle manipulation of this screw you should be able to get the horizon to make a straight line – as in (2) figure 24. Don't be unduly disappointed if you can't get rid of the index error without bringing back side error! This often happens with old sextants, and you must be content with getting rid of the side error and recording the amount of residual index error. If this residual index error amounts to less than three minutes of arc it can be accepted and allowed for in calculating every subsequent angle taken with the sextant that day. Ideally speaking, you should check for index error before taking every sight, and with practice it becomes the work of a moment. Take a quick look at the horizon through the telescope, adjust so that the horizon becomes a straight line, and read the amount of index error from the arc. This amount will either be *on the arc* or *off the arc*. There are no complications in working out whether this error should be added or subtracted to any subsequent reading: if it is to the left of zero it is *on the arc* and *minus*; if to the right of zero it is *off the arc* and *plus*.

Figure 25 shows three minutes of *on the arc* error on

my old vernier sextant. Verniers differ from instrument
to instrument: the device itself was invented by Pierre
Vernier in 1631 and consists of a small auxiliary scale
attached to the main scale so that fine readings can be
made. On my 1911 sextant the main scale is divided
into 20-minute divisions (3 per degree), and the vernier
scale into 20 minutes in whole minutes and half
minutes. In figure 25 you can see that the arrow on the
vernier falls in the first part of the main scale division
between 0° 0′ and 0° 20′. Moreover, by inspection you
can see that the reading will be somewhere in the first
quarter of this 20-minute division. By looking along
the join of the vernier and the main scale you find that
the *only* place where there is a straight line running
from the top of the main scale to the bottom of the
vernier scale is at the mark third along from the vernier

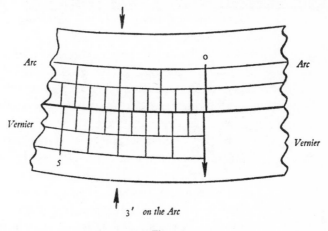

Figure 25

arrow. This makes the reading 0° 03′. Some verniers
can be read to ten seconds of arc: this is too fine for the
yachtsman – half a minute will usually suffice. With
micrometer sextants the reading of index error is simplicity itself, for an arrow gives the reading direct from
the barrel of the micrometer head. Figure 25a shows a

non-vernier head marked in minutes of arc: the reading is 60° 02′.

That ends the account of adjustable errors: the remaining three errors are worth knowing about but are difficult for the amateur to correct. If you detect them it is a dockyard job by an instrument-maker to put them right.

The fourth error is called the error of collimation. This means that the collar holding the telescope is out of alignment and that, as a rule, all your angles are working out at more than they should be. With collimation the greater the angle taken the greater the error, so pack the sextant up carefully and send it away for expert attention.

Centring error exists when the pivoting point of the index bar is not placed exactly at the centre of the arc. These errors are always extremely small and rarely exceed one minute of arc; the fault is commoner in old instruments.

Lastly there is shade error. It exists where the two faces of a shade glass are not ground parallel. Again, it is rarely found, and as rarely needs correction.

I do not recommend that you practice making physical sextant corrections for their own sake, even with the cheapest second-hand instrument, for such 'tormenting' of the sextant slackens the screws and weakens the soft metal holding the mirrors in place. The golden rule with sextants is to leave them alone as much as possible, for it is infinitely better to tolerate, and allow for, a small amount of index error than to create new sources of error through excess zeal and a passion for fiddling with the adjustment screws in an effort to squeeze out the last half minute of error.

5   *Using the sextant*

"For Heaven's sake, George! . . . it's first right past the Post Office. We're only going to the vicar's for tea!"

(By courtesy of Associated Newspapers Ltd.)

The professional seaman learns to use a sextant as a young apprentice with experienced navigators at his elbow, and he continues taking sights throughout his sea-going life. The yachtsman may not have a close relationship with his sextant until his middle years, and he often has to pick up his knowledge bit by bit from books and fellow-learners. Either way the result is the same: learning to use a sextant is like learning to ride a bicycle – difficult to learn, but hard to forget.

Start by taking a day off from work and catching a train to Brighton, Bournemouth, Eastbourne or Worthing – any seaside resort facing south with room to stand at the water's edge. Take your sextant, a note-book and pencil, a picnic lunch and a walking stick. The walking stick has two uses. If the horizon is indistinct you can dig it into the sand and use the rounded handle as a form of artificial horizon: if your apparently eccentric activities attract the attention of small boys you can brandish it in a suitably threatening manner and drive the little perishers away.

In the summertime the sun will be at its highest

point at about 1 p.m. B.S.T., and you'll want to be in position a couple of hours before then so as to be able to follow the sun's progress as it climbs in the sky, hovers for a minute or two, and then begins to fall towards the western horizon. Take the sextant out of its box without touching the arc with your fingers and hold it by the handle in your right hand. Don't ship the telescope yet. Set the index bar to zero and look towards the pier with the instrument held vertically, directing your gaze through the telescope collar and into the horizon mirror. You should see something

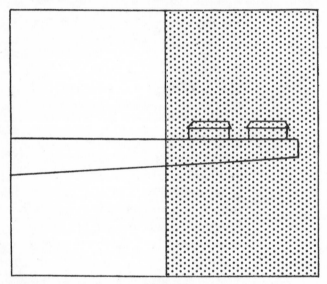

Figure 27

like the view shown in figure 27. The left-hand part of the picture is what you see straight through the un-silvered part of the horizon mirror; the right-hand part is the darkly reflected image seen through the medium of both the index and horizon mirrors.

Turn the fine adjustment screw a trifle and you'll find that the left-hand image remains stationary while the right-hand image moves up and down with the movement of the screw. Note, in particular, that as the index bar moves forward and an angle begins to register on the arc the right-hand image disappears downward from view. Now, go back to a zero setting on the arc and follow the right-hand image downwards, keeping it in the centre of the right-hand part of the mirror. When you've got into the way of bringing the right-hand image down smoothly it is time to turn your back on the sea for a while and concentrate on aligning objects with the sextant.

Assume that behind you there are two hard-edged features – such as a cliff top and a sea-wall. Focus on the line of the cliff top with the index bar set to zero, and then bring the image down slowly and steadily until it is exactly in line with the top of the sea-wall – as in figure 28. Lock the index bar and take a breather.

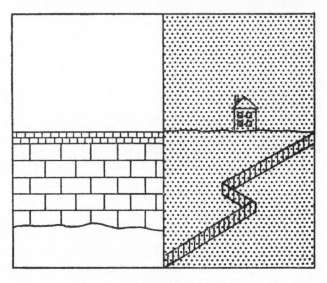

Figure 28

Then read the angle off the arc: it will be the angle between the cliff top and the sea-wall from your present position. Do it two or three times more to make

sure you're getting it right. Then ship the star telescope
(the bell-shaped one) and run through the procedure
another half a dozen times until it becomes second
nature to get the objects aligned correctly.

Turn back to the sea again. The sun should be
shining away over the horizon to the southward, and
your next task is to measure the angle between the
lower limb (or bottom edge) of the sun and the horizon.
This time you'll have to use the shades to overcome
glare. Start with the index mirror shades and try them
in turn until you find the one that makes the sun appear
as a solid disc and doesn't hurt the eyes. Then turn
down the corresponding horizon mirror shade, and
set the index bar to zero. Look at the sun through the
telescope and bring the image down to about the level
of the horizon. Flip back the horizon mirror shade

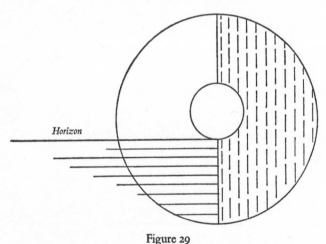

Horizon

Figure 29

so that you can see the horizon clearly, and turn the
fine adjustment screw until the bottom curve of the
sun just touches the horizon – as in figure 29. Take a
quick look at your wrist-watch, and note the angle
and the time in your notebook. Carry on taking the
angle at five minute intervals, and construct a rough

graph in your notebook as you go along: it'll show you that the sun rises to a high point with an even curve, and sinks with the same constant curvature.

The climax of this day of self-instruction comes at about 1 p.m. when you take the highest angle of the day – the meridian altitude. This particular sight is of such importance that the whole of the next chapter is devoted to it, and all I want to say now is that it gives you latitude without any element of time being involved. Because you have been taking sights at five minute intervals, and plotting them as you go along, it won't matter if you miss the actual moment when the sun is at its highest point, for the graph will give you the figure by inspection. When you get home you can get out the almanac and work out the latitude of the seaside resort where you've spent the day. If there is a large discrepancy you'll know that either your technique is wrong or the instrument needs skilled attention.

In the afternoon you will be able to experiment with a more sophisticated method for taking the angle. You will have a very fair idea of the rough angle of the sun by inspection with the naked eye. If you estimate that the angle is, say, 40°, set 40° on the sextant, point the instrument directly at the horizon and 'sweep' from side to side to catch the flash of the sun's rays in the telescope. When you have the sextant positioned vertically beneath the sun you can make fine adjustments to get the correct angle. Whichever method you use it is vital to hold the sextant absolutely vertical, otherwise there will be error in every sight you take.

During this first day the sun is your only target. On a later excursion you can try the stars and planets. Don't try and ascertain position by the moon: she moves so fast and looms so large in the sky that a small-boat navigator will find himself in a hopeless tangle to get the time right and work out the heavy corrections involved. Moon sights are ideal for examination papers and as diversion during long night watches on merchant vessels: they are of little value to yachtsmen.

It's a long road from doing sextant exercises on a coastal beach to taking sights from a small boat when out of sight of land, and I want to end this chapter with some practical advice on using a sextant at sea. In bad weather I find it best to jam the lower half of the body in a hatch in such a way that the upper part is free to sway with the roll of the ship. If your eye is only some six feet above wave level there will be difficulty in finding the true horizon, and the answer is to take the sight when the boat lifts to the top of a wave. In a 'hummocky' sea let the ship run off before the wind to provide a steady working platform, and in really bad weather have the ship hove-to and take sights from up forward with an arm round the mast to get your eye as high as possible. Don't rely on a single sight; take a series of eight and average them out. In fog and a calm sea take sights from a low point in the cockpit – there's a better horizon nearer the water. Never tell the crew 'Oh, it's too rough to use the sextant', for their morale suffers if they feel that wind and weather can interfere with position-finding. A sight with 20 miles of error is better than no sight at all.

Salt spray will ruin an instrument in three seasons: keep a piece of chamois leather in your sextant box and give the instrument a dry wipe after use. Pay particular attention to the mirrors, for damp will take off the silvering in very short order. If the arc gets worn use a mixture of soot and olive oil to 'bring out' the markings. Finally, never leave the sextant on a bunk – someone is sure to sit on it. Put it away in the box after use, and stow the box in a locker fitted with a retaining bar so that it is held rigid, stands right way up and is out of harm's way.

6   *Noon sights for latitude*

'All in a hot and copper sky,
The bloody Sun at noon,
Right above the mast did stand,
No bigger than the moon.'
Coleridge: *The Rime of the Ancient Mariner*

Let me start with an easy example. You are the navigator of a yacht bound from the Solent towards Le Havre on the 28th of June. There isn't a cloud in the sky, and you go up on deck at about half past twelve British Summer Time with a sextant, your copy of *Reed's Nautical Almanac*, a pencil and a scrap of paper. Check the index error of the sextant, and then take a look at the compass and note that the sun's true bearing is a bit east of south. Take two or three trial altitudes of the sun's lower limb and notice that the angle is still increasing. Keep on taking the angle at regular intervals, and between observations look in the almanac to find out the time of the sun's meridian passage, or highest point. Look at page 42 (or Table 1 in this book) and find under the heading 'Sun' a column marked 'Transit'. You'll see that for 28th June the time of transit is given as 1203 Greenwich Mean Time. Add one hour for British Summer Time and stand by to get the angle at 1303 BST by your wrist-watch.

In this case the yacht is sailing along pretty close to the meridian of Greenwich and you take the figure straight from the almanac. If you're not close to the prime meridian you must convert the longitude into time by a simple table found on pages 154–155. Suppose your dead reckoning longitude is 11° 18′ W. You enter the table at the left of the page for 11° and

find it converts to 44 minutes of time. At the other side
of the page 18 minutes of arc convert to 1 minute, 12
seconds of time. The rule for applying the longitude is
that westerly longitude is *added*: easterly longitude is
subtracted. So, you take 1203 GMT as the time of transit
on the Greenwich meridian, add 44 minutes and 1
minute, making 1248 GMT, and then an hour for BST.
That makes 1348 BST the time to take the angle of the
sun's meridian passage when in DR longitude 11° 18′
on 28th June.

However, in our simple example the almanac figure
needs no such correction, and in due course you get the
angle of 63° 21′ on the sextant arc. This angle is the
Sun's Observed Meridian Altitude and the first thing
to do is to correct it for index error, thus:

$$\begin{aligned}
\text{Observed Meridian Altitude} &= 63° \ 21′ \\
\text{Index Error} &= \qquad -2′ \\
\hline
\text{Corrected Sun's Mer. Alt} &= 63° \ 19′
\end{aligned}$$

The next step is to allow for some small differences
due to the dip of the sea horizon, refraction, parallax
and semi-diameter. Before your eyes glaze over and
you reach forward for the knob on the television set
let me point out that all these factors are catered for in
a simple combined table. Figure 30 depicts such a table;
another may be found in *Reed's* on page 86 or on a
loose card supplied with the almanac. A brief explanation of the four items allowed for in the total correction table follows. Dip is due to the height of eye
above sea level at the time of taking the observation:
refraction is due to the bending of light rays near the
horizon. Semi-diameter must be allowed for because
we are sighting on the edge of the sun and not on its
centre, while parallax exists because we are working
from the surface of the earth and not from its centre.

Figure 30.

CORRECTION TABLE: TRUE ALTITUDE FROM OBSERVED ALTITUDE

All figures are in minutes and decimals of minutes

SUN
ALWAYS ADDED (+)

STAR
ALWAYS SUBTRACTED (−)

Observed altitude in whole degrees	Height of eye in feet				Observed altitude in whole degrees	Height of eye in feet			
	4	6	8	12		4	6	8	12
7	6.7	6.3	5.9	5.2	7	9.4	9.7	10.3	10.9
8	7.5	7.1	6.7	6.1	8	8.5	8.8	9.4	10.0
9	8.2	7.9	7.6	7.0	9	7.8	8.2	8.7	9.4
10	8.7	8.5	8.1	7.5	10	7.1	7.7	8.2	8.8
11	9.1	8.9	8.6	7.9	11	6.6	7.1	7.6	8.3
12	9.5	9.3	8.9	8.3	12	6.3	6.8	7.3	7.9
13	9.9	9.7	9.3	8.6	13	6.0	6.5	7.0	7.6
14	10.2	10.0	9.6	8.9	14	5.8	6.2	6.6	7.3
15	10.5	10.2	9.9	9.2	15	5.5	5.9	6.4	7.0
16	10.8	10.4	10.0	9.6	16	5.2	5.7	6.2	6.8
17	10.9	10.7	10.3	9.7	17	5.0	5.5	6.0	6.6
18	11.1	10.8	10.5	9.8	18	4.9	5.3	5.8	6.4
19	11.2	11.0	10.6	10.0	19	4.7	5.1	5.6	6.2
20	11.4	11.2	10.8	10.2	20	4.6	5.0	5.4	6.1
21	11.5	11.3	10.9	10.3	21	4.4	4.9	5.3	6.0
22	11.6	11.4	11.0	10.4	22	4.3	4.7	5.2	5.8
23	11.7	11.5	11.1	10.5	23	4.2	4.6	5.1	5.7
24	11.9	11.6	11.2	10.6	24	4.1	4.5	5.0	5.6
25	12.0	11.7	11.3	10.7	25	4.0	4.4	4.9	5.5
26	12.0	11.8	11.4	10.8	26	3.9	4.4	4.8	5.5
27	12.1	11.9	11.5	10.9	27	3.8	4.3	4.7	5.4
28	12.1	12.0	11.6	11.0	28	3.7	4.2	4.6	5.3
29	12.2	12.0	11.7	11.0	29	3.6	4.1	4.5	5.2
30	12.3	12.1	11.8	11.1	30	3.6	4.0	4.5	5.1
32	12.4	12.2	11.9	11.2	32	3.5	3.9	4.4	5.0
34	12.5	12.3	12.0	11.3	34	3.4	3.8	4.3	4.9
36	12.6	12.4	12.1	11.4	36	3.3	3.7	4.2	4.8
38	12.7	12.5	12.1	11.4	38	3.2	3.6	4.1	4.7
40	12.8	12.6	12.2	11.6	40	3.1	3.5	4.0	4.6
42	12.9	12.7	12.3	11.7	42	3.1	3.5	3.9	4.5
44	12.9	12.7	12.4	11.7	44	3.0	3.4	3.8	4.5
46	13.0	12.8	12.4	11.8	46	3.0	3.4	3.8	4.4
48	13.0	12.9	12.5	11.9	48	2.9	3.3	3.7	4.3
50	13.1	12.9	12.5	11.9	50	2.8	3.2	3.7	4.2
54	13.3	13.0	12.6	12.0	54	2.7	3.1	3.6	4.1
58	13.4	13.1	12.7	12.1	58	2.6	3.0	3.5	4.0
62	13.5	13.2	12.8	12.2	62	2.5	2.9	3.4	4.0
66	13.6	13.2	12.9	12.3	66	2.4	2.8	3.3	3.9
70	13.7	13.3	13.0	12.4	70	2.3	2.7	3.2	3.8
80	13.8	13.5	13.1	12.5	80	2.1	2.5	3.0	3.6
90	13.9	13.6	13.2	12.6	90	2.0	2.4	2.8	3.4

The following monthly corrections FOR THE SUN ONLY are optional:

Jan.	Feb.	March	April	May	June	July	August	Sept.	Oct.	Nov.	Dec.
+0.3	+0.2	+0.1	NIL	−0.1	−0.2	−0.2	−0.2	+0.1	+0.1	+0.2	+0.3

G.M.T.	SUN G.H.A.	Dec.	ARIES G.H.A.	G.M.T.	SUN G.H.A.	Dec.	ARIES G.H.A.	G.M.T.	SUN G.H.A.	Dec.	ARIES G.H.A.	G.M.T.

Sunday, 16th June   **Friday, 21st June**   **Wednesday, 26th June**

h	SUN G.H.A.	Dec.	ARIES G.H.A.	h	SUN G.H.A.	Dec.	ARIES G.H.A.	h	SUN G.H.A.	Dec.	ARIES G.H.A.	h
00	179 52·6N23	20·8	264 19·4	00	179 36·4N23	24·7	269 15·1	00	179 20·2N23	22·3	274 10·8	00
02	209 52·4 23	21·0	294 24·3	02	209 36·1 23	24·7	299 20·0	02	209 19·9 23	22·1	304 15·7	02
04	239 52·1 23	21·2	324 29·3	04	239 35·8 23	24·7	329 24·9	04	239 19·7 23	21·9	334 20·6	04
06	269 51·8 23	21·4	354 34·2	06	269 35·6 23	24·7	359 29·9	06	269 19·4 23	21·8	4 25·6	06
08	299 51·6 23	21·6	24 39·1	08	299 35·3 23	24·7	29 34·8	08	299 19·1 23	21·6	34 30·5	08
10	329 51·3 23	21·7	54 44·0	10	329 35·0 23	24·7	59 39·7	10	329 18·9 23	21·4	64 35·4	10
12	359 51·0 23	21·9	84 49·0	12	359 34·8 23	24·7	89 44·7	12	359 18·6 23	21·3	94 40·4	12
14	29 50·8 23	22·1	114 53·9	14	29 34·5 23	24·7	119 49·6	14	29 18·3 23	21·1	124 45·3	14
16	59 50·5 23	22·2	144 58·8	16	59 34·2 23	24·7	149 54·5	16	59 18·1 23	20·9	154 50·2	16
18	89 50·2 23	22·4	175 03·8	18	89 33·9 23	24·7	179 59·4	18	89 17·8 23	20·7	184 55·1	18
20	119 50·0 23	22·5	205 08·7	20	119 33·7 23	24·7	210 04·4	20	119 17·6 23	20·5	215 00·1	20
22	149 49·7N23	22·7	235 13·6	22	149 33·4N23	24·7	240 09·3	22	149 17·3N23	20·3	245 05·0	22

Monday, 17th June   **Saturday, 22nd June**   **Thursday, 27th June**

00	179 49·4N23	22·8	265 18·5	00	179 33·1N23	24·7	270 14·2	00	179 17·0N23	20·1	275 09·9	00
02	209 49·2 23	23·0	295 23·5	02	209 32·9 23	24·6	300 19·1	02	209 16·8 23	19·9	305 14·9	02
04	239 48·9 23	23·1	325 28·4	04	239 32·6 23	24·6	330 24·1	04	239 16·5 23	19·7	335 19·8	04
06	269 48·6 23	23·3	355 33·3	06	269 32·3 23	24·6	0 29·0	06	269 16·2 23	19·5	5 24·7	06
08	299 48·4 23	23·4	25 38·2	08	299 32·0 23	24·5	30 33·9	08	299 16·0 23	19·3	35 29·6	08
10	329 48·1 23	23·6	55 43·2	10	329 31·8 23	24·5	60 38·9	10	329 15·7 23	19·1	65 34·6	10
12	359 47·8 23	23·7	85 48·1	12	359 31·5 23	24·5	90 43·8	12	359 15·5 23	18·9	95 39·5	12
14	29 47·5 23	23·8	115 53·0	14	29 31·2 23	24·4	120 48·7	14	29 15·2 23	18·7	125 44·4	14
16	59 47·3 23	23·9	145 58·0	16	59 31·0 23	24·4	150 53·6	16	59 14·9 23	18·5	155 49·4	16
18	89 47·0 23	24·1	176 02·9	18	89 30·7 23	24·3	180 58·6	18	89 14·7 23	18·3	185 54·3	18
20	119 46·7 23	24·2	206 07·8	20	119 30·4 23	24·3	211 03·5	20	119 14·4 23	18·1	215 59·2	20
22	149 46·5N23	24·3	236 12·7	22	149 30·1N23	24·2	241 08·4	22	149 14·2N23	17·8	246 04·1	22

Tuesday, 18th June   **Sunday, 23rd June**   **Friday, 28th June**

00	179 46·2N23	24·4	266 17·7	00	179 29·9N23	24·2	271 13·4	00	179 13·9N23	17·6	276 09·1	00
02	209 45·9 23	24·5	296 22·6	02	209 29·6 23	24·1	301 18·3	02	209 13·7 23	17·4	306 14·0	02
04	239 45·6 23	24·7	326 27·5	04	239 29·3 23	24·1	331 23·2	04	239 13·4 23	17·1	336 18·9	04
06	269 45·4 23	24·8	356 32·5	06	269 29·1 23	24·0	1 28·1	06	269 13·1 23	16·9	6 23·9	06
08	299 45·1 23	24·9	26 37·4	08	299 28·8 23	25·9	31 33·1	08	299 12·9 23	16·7	36 28·8	08
10	329 44·8 23	25·0	56 42·3	10	329 28·5 23	25·9	61 38·0	10	329 12·6 23	16·4	66 33·7	10
12	359 44·6 23	25·1	86 47·2	12	359 28·2 23	25·8	91 42·9	12	359 12·4 23	16·2	96 38·6	12
14	29 44·3 23	25·2	116 52·2	14	29 28·0 23	25·7	121 47·9	14	29 12·1 23	15·9	126 43·6	14
16	59 44·0 23	25·3	146 57·1	16	59 27·7 23	25·6	151 52·8	16	59 11·9 23	15·7	156 48·5	16
18	89 43·8 23	25·4	177 02·0	18	89 27·4 23	25·6	181 57·7	18	89 11·6 23	15·4	186 53·4	18
20	119 43·5 23	25·4	207 06·9	20	119 27·2 23	25·5	212 02·6	20	119 11·4 23	15·2	216 58·4	20
22	149 43·2N23	25·5	237 11·9	22	149 26·9N23	25·4	242 07·6	22	149 11·1N23	14·9	247 03·3	22

Wednesday, 19th June   **Monday, 24th June**   **Saturday, 29th June**

00	179 42·9N23	25·6	267 16·8	00	179 26·6N23	25·3	272 12·5	00	179 10·8N23	14·7	277 08·2	00
02	209 42·7 23	25·7	297 21·7	02	209 26·3 23	25·2	302 17·4	02	209 10·6 23	14·4	307 13·1	02
04	239 42·4 23	25·8	327 26·7	04	239 26·1 23	25·1	332 22·4	04	239 10·3 23	14·1	337 18·1	04
06	269 42·1 23	25·8	357 31·6	06	269 25·8 23	25·0	2 27·3	06	269 10·1 23	13·9	7 23·0	06
08	299 41·8 23	25·9	27 36·5	08	299 25·5 23	24·9	32 32·2	08	299 09·8 23	13·6	37 27·9	08
10	329 41·6 23	26·0	57 41·4	10	329 25·3 23	24·8	62 37·1	10	329 09·6 23	13·3	67 32·9	10
12	359 41·3 23	26·0	87 46·4	12	359 25·0 23	24·7	92 42·1	12	359 09·3 23	13·0	97 37·8	12
14	29 41·0 23	26·1	117 51·3	14	29 24·7 23	24·6	122 47·0	14	29 09·1 23	12·8	127 42·7	14
16	59 40·8 23	26·2	147 56·2	16	59 24·5 23	24·5	152 51·9	16	59 08·8 23	12·5	157 47·6	16
18	89 40·5 23	26·2	178 01·2	18	89 24·2 23	24·4	182 56·9	18	89 08·6 23	12·2	187 52·6	18
20	119 40·2 23	26·3	208 06·1	20	119 23·9 23	24·2	213 01·8	20	119 08·3 23	11·9	217 57·5	20
22	149 39·9N23	26·3	238 11·0	22	149 23·7N23	24·1	243 06·7	22	149 08·1N23	11·6	248 02·4	22

Thursday, 20th June   **Tuesday, 25th June**   **Sunday, 30th June**

00	179 39·7N23	26·4	268 15·9	00	179 23·4N23	24·0	273 11·6	00	179 07·8N23	11·3	278 07·4	00
02	209 39·4 23	26·4	298 20·9	02	209 23·1 23	23·9	303 16·6	02	209 07·6 23	11·0	308 12·3	02
04	239 39·1 23	26·5	328 25·8	04	239 22·9 23	23·7	333 21·5	04	239 07·3 23	10·7	338 17·2	04
06	269 38·8 23	26·5	358 30·7	06	269 22·6 23	23·6	3 26·4	06	269 07·1 23	10·4	8 22·1	06
08	299 38·6 23	26·5	28 35·7	08	299 22·3 23	23·5	33 31·4	08	299 06·8 23	10·1	38 27·1	08
10	329 38·3 23	26·6	58 40·6	10	329 22·0 23	23·3	63 36·3	10	329 06·6 23	09·8	68 32·0	10
12	359 38·0 23	26·6	88 45·5	12	359 21·8 23	23·2	93 41·2	12	359 06·3 23	09·5	98 36·9	12
14	29 37·8 23	26·6	118 50·4	14	29 21·5 23	23·0	123 46·1	14	29 06·1 23	09·2	128 41·8	14
16	59 37·5 23	26·7	148 55·4	16	59 21·3 23	22·9	153 51·1	16	59 05·8 23	08·8	158 46·8	16
18	89 37·2 23	26·7	179 00·3	18	89 21·0 23	22·7	183 56·0	18	89 05·6 23	08·5	188 51·7	18
20	119 36·9 23	26·7	209 05·2	20	119 20·7 23	22·6	214 00·9	20	119 05·4 23	08·2	218 56·6	20
22	149 36·7N23	26·7	239 10·2	22	149 20·5N23	22·4	244 05·9	22	149 05·1N23	07·9	249 01·6	22

Figure 31

The total correction table is easy to use: you enter at the top with the estimated height of your eye in feet above water level, match it with the figure of the observed meridian altitude in whole degrees on the left-hand side and read off the correction, interpolating mentally if necessary. In this case the height of eye is 8 feet and the correction + 12.8′. The sum continues:

Corrected Sun's Mer. Alt. =	63° 19′ (s)	NOTE: South
Total Correction =	+ 12.8′	because the
Monthly Correction =	− 0.2′	sun bore
	————	southerly
True Altitude =	63° 31.6′(s)	when sight
	————	taken.

Stop there a second and look back to figure 19. We have the true altitude of the sun: what we want is the zenith distance. To get it we subtract the true altitude from 90°, thus:

	90° 00′	
True Altitude =	63° 31.6′ (s)	
	————	
Zenith Distance =	26° 28.4′ (N)	NOTE: The sign is
	————	changed on sub-
		tracting the true
		altitude from 90°.

Only one more operation. The sun's declination must be applied to the zenith distance to get the latitude. The figure for the declination is found on the fourth monthly page for June (see figure 31) under the entry for 28th June. The third column has the declination in black type at two-hour intervals. The declination comes out as N 23° 16.2′, and the sum ends:

Zenith Distance =	26° 28.4′ (N)	*Note:* By rule:
Declination =	23° 16.2′ (N)	same names add,
	————	different names
Latitude =	49° 44.6′	subtract and name
	————	as the greater.

It all looks very complicated because I have gone through each step in detail. However, if you compress it the sum looks like this:

Observed meridian altitude	=	63° 21′
Index error	=	− 2′
Corrected Sun's Mer. Alt.	=	63° 19′ (s)
Total correction table	=	+ 12.6′ (includes monthly figure)
True Altitude	=	63° 31.6′ (s)

$$90° \ 00'$$
$$63° \ 31.6'$$

Zenith distance	=	26° 28.4′ (N)
Declination	=	23° 16.2′ (N)

Latitude = 49° 44.6′ North

One final simplification. If you have most of the data all written out beforehand the paperwork looks something like this:

$$90° \ 00'$$

Total correction (reversed) = − 12.6′

$$89° \ 47.4'$$

Declination = 23° 16.2′ ADD

$$113° \ 3.6'$$

Angle = 63° 19.0′ SUBTRACT

Latitude = 49° 44.6′

Plotting a position line obtained from noon sights is a simple affair. Lay your parallel ruler along a line of latitude marked on the chart and carry the other leg (or edge) of the ruler up to the appropriate latitude figure on the scale at the side of the chart. Make your position line reasonably long and enter the time alongside in preparation for carrying it forward to 'cross' it with a line obtained by other means to get a 'fix'.

Try the following problems using Table I, figures 30 and 31, and the Arc/Time table on pages 154–5 in *Reed's*.

    1. On 16th June in DR position 49° 59′ N, 6° 50′ W find (1) the GMT for taking the meridian altitude of the sun, and (2) the latitude if the sextant reading is 62° 01′, the index error nil and the height of eye 12 feet.

    2. On 18th June in DR position 54° 25′ N, 3° 30′ E find (1) the CET(BST) for taking the meridian altitude of the sun, and (2) the latitude if the sextant reading is 58° 46′, the index error +0.9′, and the height of eye 6 feet.

    3. On 26th June in DR position 47° 36.5′ N, 7° 35′ W find (1) the GMT for taking the meridian altitude of the sun, and (2) the latitude if the sextant reading is 65° 39′, the index error + 2.1′, and the height of eye 8 feet.

Answers page 116

This sight has only one limitation. Vessels navigating near the equator will find the sextant angle sometimes gets so close to 90° that it is virtually impossible to take the angle properly, and star sights have to be used instead. It happened to me once when sailing off Trinidad: I found it very disconcerting. In British waters, however, the sun is always at a useful angle at noon, and this valuable check on distance and progress should never be omitted or neglected. I mentioned at the beginning of this book that Voss made an Australian port by latitude and the set of the ocean swell when his compass was lost. A similar feat was accomplished in 1923 by the shipwrecked crew of the S.S.

Trevessa who made a voyage of 1,700 miles in open boats without a chronometer when their vessel sank in the middle of the Indian Ocean. The captain's account† lays stress on the value of noon sights in such circumstances. The possession of a sextant and the knowledge of the latitude of the destination was backed up by the sheer guts of the officers commanding the clumsy open lifeboats, and these three factors taken together saved the lives of thirty-three men.

† *The Loss of the Trevessa* by Cecil Foster.

Pole star for latitude

'Twinkle, twinkle, polar star,
I can see how bright you are.
Right above the north, so high,
Like a signpost in the sky.'
Anon

Polaris is the most useful star in the northern hemisphere. It stands almost exactly at the pole of the sky –
the centre around which the stars appear to be revolv-
ing – and is virtually due north from the observer at
any time it is visible. It is bright, easily found by
reference to other stars, and, in British waters, is
positioned about half-way between the horizon and
the zenith so that its angle can readily be taken with a
sextant.

To find Polaris in the night sky you must first find
the constellation called the Plough. If you look north
you'll see the Plough wheeling around the pole star in
a slow circle. The two stars forming the blade of the
Plough point to Polaris (see figure 32), and if you
prolong an imaginary line joining these two stars by
an amount approximating to five times the distance
between them your eye will fall on Polaris. The two
stars are called 'The Pointers', and it doesn't matter
what hour of the night you are looking for Polaris –
'The Pointers' will always show the way.

Polaris can give you the latitude at any time it is
visible from evening twilight to sunrise. Because its
true bearing is always within a degree or two of true
north you don't have to apply many corrections to the
sextant reading to get the latitude. In fact, you can put
the dead reckoning latitude on the arc before starting

to take the sight, confident that the reading will not greatly differ from that figure. The very best time to take a sight of Polaris is during morning and evening

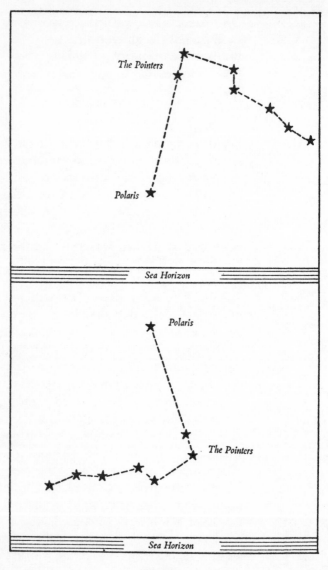

Figure 32

twilight when the stars are out and the horizon is still clearly defined: the next best is when the moon shines well enough to give you a horizon, but is not so bright that it blots out the stars altogether.

Before getting down to the nuts and bolts of obtaining the latitude from the pole star I have to introduce you to four new expressions. They are the First Point of Aries, the Greenwich Hour Angle of Aries, the Local Hour Angle of Aries and Sidereal Hour Angle.

The First Point of Aries is an astronomical fiction: it is an imaginary point on the celestial sphere used to fix relative positions. I always think of it as a man-made

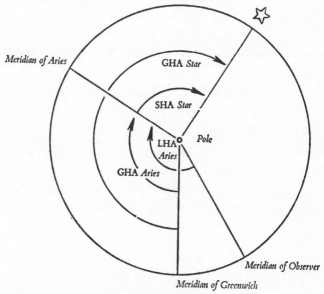

Figure 33

heavenly body which is quoted in the almanac as if it was a star. To understand the static role of Aries look at figure 33 and follow the reasoning. The hour angle of a heavenly body has the same relationship to longitude as declination has to latitude. The differences are that hour angle is always measured westerly; it does not stop at 180° but goes right round to 360°, and it can be expressed in both time and arc. Hour angle comes in a number of different packets: the first one dealt with here is the Greenwich Hour Angle of Aries. GHA Aries is the angle at the pole measured westerly from the Greenwich meridian to the meridian of the geographical position of Aries. Local Hour Angle is also measured westerly, but the starting point is the meridian of the observer. LHA Aries, therefore, is the angle at the pole, measured westerly, from the meridian of the observer – his dead reckoning longitude – to the meridian of the geographical position of Aries. The whole point of obtaining LHA Aries is so that we can enter a special table in *Reed's Nautical Almanac* (page 91), and get the correction to the observed altitude of Polaris. LHA Aries is found by the following simple formula:

$$\text{GHA Aries} + \begin{array}{l} \text{East longitude} \\ - \text{ West longitude} \end{array} = \text{LHA Aries}$$

Another glance at figure 33, and using the sun as an example, should help you to grasp this point. Obviously, if the meridian of the observer is east of Greenwich (as in the illustration) the LHA is greater than the GHA because the sun has passed the observer first. Conversely, if you are west of Greenwich LHA is less than GHA. Although it does not affect Polaris sights this figure should also help you to understand Sidereal Hour Angle (SHA). The SHA of a star runs westerly from the meridian of Aries (our 'static' point, remember) round to the meridian of the geographical position of the star, and, of course, the GHA of a star is found in the same way as the GHA of Aries: you start at the Greenwich meridian and go round the circle of degrees westerly until you come to the meridian of the star concerned.

Let me go through a practical example of using Polaris to get position. You are the navigator of a yacht that left Ramsgate during the morning of the 27th June, bound for the Hook of Holland. There's a south-westerly blowing, and the yacht has made good progress to the east-north-east in poor visibility, having sighted nothing since leaving North Foreland over the stern. At 0320 GMT on the 28th, when in DR position 51° 53′ N, 3° 30′ E, the cloud cover clears momentarily and you get an angle for Polaris of 52° 20′ on your sextant. The instrument is free from error, and the height of your eye when taking the observation was ten feet. What is the latitude?

Look at figure 31 again and find the 28th June. The GHA of Aries at 0200 GMT is 306° 14.0′. The correction table for GHA Aries on page 89 of the almanac gives the addition for one hour and twenty minutes as 20° 3.3′. The sum begins:

GHA Aries at 0200   306°   14.0′
Correction for 1 hour, 20 mins.   + 20°   3.3′
_____
GHA Aries at 0320 GMT   326°   17.3′
_____

Now to find the LHA Aries by the rule ... LHA Aries = GHA Aries + Easterly longitude ...

GHA Aries at 0330 GMT   326°   17.3′
Easterly longitude (+)   3°   30.0′
_____
LHA Aries at 0320 GMT   329°   47.3′
_____

At this stage we leave LHA Aries on one side and go back to the observed altitude of Polaris, which was 52° 20′. No correction is needed for index error, but we must make allowances for refraction and dip of the horizon (or height of eye). The correction table appears on page 87 and as Table 2 in this book: it is always subtractive. By entering the star altitude total correction table with height of eye and the approximate figure of the sight we get a correction of $-3.8'$. So, we continue:

Observed altitude Polaris	52° 20′
Star total correction	−3.8′
True altitude of Polaris	52° 16.2′

Now use the figure for LHA Aries to enter the last table for pole star correction (page 91). The sum ends

True altitude of Polaris	52° 16.2′
Pole star correction	−23.8′
LATITUDE	51° 52.4′

This sight puts the yacht on the same latitude as the north shore of Goeree, about some ten miles south and west of the Hook of Holland entrance. The large-scale charts tell you that there is a row of buoys like a picket fence along that coast leading the big ships towards the Hook and the port of Rotterdam. Feeling satisfied with your Polaris sight (for it squares nicely with your dead reckoning latitude), and conscious always of the need to stay up-wind of a destination, you alter course to due east with the intention of staying on that parallel of latitude until getting a 'fix' from shore-marks or a heavenly body.

As with the noon sight in the last chapter the working of the example compresses to much less figuring than has been shown here. End by trying this one for yourself: On 19th June at 2331 GMT in DR position 50° 03′ N, 9° 35′ W an observer in a yacht whose height of eye was five feet took the sextant angle of Polaris and found it to be 49° 20′. The sextant is free from error. What is the latitude? *Answer page 116.*

8 *The astronomical position line*

'In November 1837, Captain Thomas H. Sumner, from Charleston, South Carolina, bound for Greenock, and being by DR within about forty miles of the Tuskar Light, got an altitude of the sun at about 10 a.m., no subsequent observation being possible. The latitude was quite uncertain owing to several days of thick weather. This sight was worked out several times with different assumed latitudes, and it was found that the positions when plotted on a chart all lay in a straight line. Captain Sumner then realized that his single observation had given him, independently of the latitude, a line on which the ship must be situated somewhere.'

Claud Worth: *Yacht Navigation and Voyaging*

Captain Sumner published details of his discovery in 1843, pointing out that the true bearing of the sun at the time of the observation was always at right angles to the position line. Other navigators, of whom Admiral Marcq Saint-Hilaire was the most eminent, adapted and modified Sumner's original discovery, with the result that the astronomical position line method of obtaining position from the observation of heavenly bodies is that most commonly used at sea today. The differences between the various ways of setting about it are due to the variety of tables in use.

Look back at figures 12–14 and fix the appearance of the position circle, the geographical position and the position line in your mind's eye. You will recall that the sextant angle gives the observer his observed zenith distance and the size of the position circle. By calculation the observer can work out his calculated zenith distance from his dead reckoning position. The two will rarely agree, for the dead reckoning position chosen is generally too near to or too far away from the body's geographical position. The difference between the calculated zenith distance and the observed zenith distance is called the INTERCEPT, and it enables the observer to fix the location of the position line in relation to the DR position. Look at figure 34 and follow the reasoning.

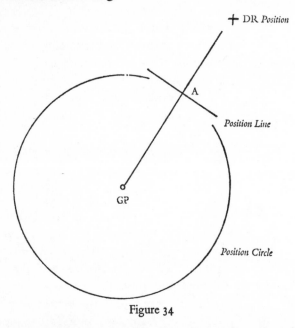

Figure 34

The line from the dead reckoning position to the body's geographical position represents the azimuth, or bearing, of the heavenly body at the time of taking the observation. It also represents the calculated zenith distance (CZD). At the point 'A' where it crosses the position circle I have straightened out a part of the circle to make a position line. The observed zenith distance (OZD) runs from 'A' to the geographical position, and the portion from 'A' to the DR position is the intercept. In this case the intercept is 'towards' because the position line lies between the DR position and the geographical position and the CZD is greater than the OZD. In figure 35 you can see the situation

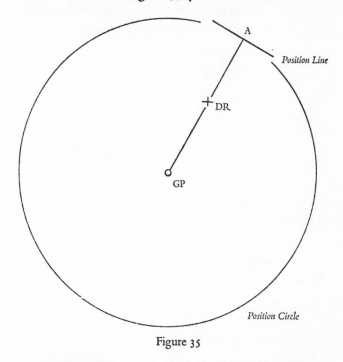

A

Position Line

+ DR

○ GP

Position Circle

Figure 35

where the intercept is 'away' and the OZD is greater than the CZD. I use the mnemonic 'FOG' to remember which is which. It stands for *F*rom (meaning 'away') *O*bserved *G*reater. No doubt, you can find one similar to suit yourself.

When it comes to actually plotting on a chart or plain paper you set about it by drawing a line from the DR position in the direction of the observed body, and carrying it through the DR position the other way as well in case it should prove to be an 'away' intercept. The whole purpose of position line navigation – all that angle-taking, table-scanning and feverish addition

The astronomical position line and subtraction – is to work out the intercept in nautical miles and plot it 'towards' or 'away' to get the point where you draw in the position line at right angles to the azimuth. Note here that the point of intersection of the line of azimuth and the position line is, in general, NOT the position of the yacht. It is the

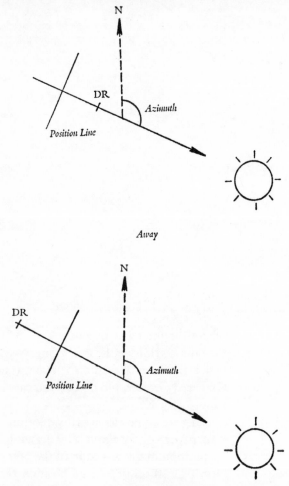

Away

Towards

Figure 36

line that is important, not the point. Look, now, at figure 36: it depicts the 'towards' and 'away' intercepts in their simplest forms.

When you have obtained your position line you can use it in several ways. If it runs in a north-east to south-west direction (as with forenoon sights) it can be 'crossed' with the noon latitude sight to get a 'fix'. If the land comes into view after an observation has been taken the position line can be brought forward to 'cross' with a line of bearing from the compass. It can be used in conjunction with a position line from another heavenly body to get a 'fix', or with a radio bearing from a shore station. These position lines are like certain exotic fruits – they won't go 'off' unless you keep them longer than 24 hours. Provided that you're careful in carrying lines forward by DR and plot them accurately they'll last well into the next day.

The sequence I follow goes like this:

Action	*Comment*
1. Body observed Height of eye Log reading ARE Index error NOTED Course made good. DR lat: DR long.	This is 'background' data: I find it easier to write it down before starting to take a sight.
2. Find the Greenwich Date.	This may sound a bit odd to the yachtsman taking sights by day near the meridian of Greenwich, but it can be important when you're a long way east or west of Greenwich. Finding the Greenwich date is dealt with in detail in chapter thirteen.

3. Take the angle.

Write it down as soon as possible!

4. Note the exact GMT at the time of taking the angle.

More about time in chapter thirteen.

5. Correct the sextant angle for index error, apply the total correction figure, then subtract from 90° to get the Observed Zenith Distance.

6. Obtain the GHA of the body observed, and turn it into LHA.

7. Note the declination of the body from the almanac.

8. Enter the tables with the LHA, the DR latitude and the declination to obtain the Calculated Zenith Distance.

See chapter nine.

9. Compare the OZD and CZD and obtain the intercept.

Make sure you name the intercept correctly!

10. Obtain azimuth of body.

See chapter nine.

11. Plot the position line.

On charts – see chapters ten, eleven and twelve: on squared paper or on a plotting chart – see chapter fourteen.

In the next chapter we'll run through the mechanics of getting the intercept and azimuth by use of the

The astronomical position line Versine and the ABC tables. The important thing to get from this chapter is an understanding of the intercept, and sure knowledge of the way to apply it.

9 *Turning the tables*

'... it is the man who writes the Navigation Tables who must be the mathematician, not the navigator who merely uses them.'

M. J. Rantzen: *Little Ship Astro-Navigation*

At the beginning of the book I made a brief reference to the spherical triangle, and while I don't want to dangle that fearsome creature before you for too long it is necessary to explain that the navigation tables used to find position from the altitude of heavenly bodies are a form of shorthand for obtaining the length of the sides, or the angles, in a spherical triangle. In this chapter I want to show you how to use the Versine and Cosine Tables in *Reed's Nautical Almanac* for getting the Calculated Zenith Distance (c z d), and run through a practical example so that we end up with the intercept and the azimuth.

These tables are compact, easy to understand and simple to work from; let me explain the use of the Versine Table first. The whole degrees are at the top of each page, or portion of each page, from 0° to 179°, and at the foot of the page, or portion of a page, from 180° to 359°. The minutes run from top to bottom on the left up to 60°, and from bottom to top on the right from 0° to 60°. Each double column contains log versines in heavy black type and natural versines in lighter type. The prefix number is not given for every column, but can easily be found by inspection in adjacent columns, and in the upper register you will have to interpolate mentally where not all the minute figures are given. Now for a dummy run. Look up the log versine of 20° 29': it is given in the penultimate column as 8.8009. Now try for the log versine of 20° 29.7'. By interpolating mentally you'll find it is 8.8014. To find the angle from the natural versine you have to hunt through the table until you find the figure, and then read off the corresponding angle from top and left or bottom and right. For instance, on this same page

SIGHT FORM

Date	Ht of Eye	Body Observed	Course	Log
18 July	6	L.L. Sun	045°T	193
D R Latitude		D R Longitude		G M T
50° 15' N		9° 30'W		07.45.57

		°	'			°	'
GHA (two-hourly figure)		268	28.4	Sextant Angle		25	35
Correction (hr and mins)		15	00.0	Index Error			+ 1.1
Correction (seconds)		11	15.0	Total Corr.			+ 11.8
			14.3				
GHA		294	57.7	TRUE ALT		25	47.9
Longitude W		9	30.0			90°	00.0'
LHA(W)		285	27.7	TRUE ALT		25	47.9
or LHA(E)				(OZD)		64	12.1

	°	'		
LHA W	285	27.7	Log Versine	9.8653
D R Lat N	50	15.0	Log Cosine	9.8058
Dec N	21	00.2	Log Cosine	9.9702
			Log Versine (2)	9.6413
Lat (+/-) N	50	15.0	Nat Versine	0.4378
Dec N	21	00.2	+	
	29	14.8 =	Nat Versine	0.1275
			Nat Versine	0.5653
			CZD	64° 14'

OZD 64 12.1
CZD 64 14.0
INTERCEPT 1.9 Towards ~~Away~~

	°	'		
D R Lat	50	15.0 N		
LHA	285	27.7 W	Table A gives	+ 0.335
Dec	21	00.2 N	Table B gives	− 0.398
				− 0.063	Table C gives	87.7

AZIMUTH = N 88°E or 088 °T

Figure 37

you'll find by inspection that 0.0574 in the natural versine column gives an angle of 19° 30′.

The Cosine Table is much easier to understand. You just enter at the top of the single column for whole degrees, and take the minutes from the left-hand side. Ignore the log sines at the foot of each page: they don't come into the picture at all.

A set working sequence is essential for getting the correct figures on which the plotting of the astronomical position line will be based. A sight form is shown on page 187 in *Reed's Nautical Almanac*: I have used a simplified version – which is shown in figure 37 – and entered an example on it. Follow through with me, keeping an eye on the text, a finger on the item in the form, and *Reed's* open before you.

In this case the navigator in a yacht sailing in the Western Approaches, whose dead reckoning position is 50° 15′ N, 9° 30′ W, gets the angle of the sun's lower limb as 25° 35′ at 07.45.57 GMT on the 18th July. The index error of his sextant is + 1.1′, and his height of eye at the time of taking the observation is 6 feet. Find the intercept and the azimuth.

The first part of the form contains the background data, and you fill it in before taking the sight. The only item you can't enter yet is the exact GMT when the sight was taken: usually you will write it down as soon as you get below and seat yourself at the chart table.

I suggest you deal with the sextant angle first, entering the figures in the right-hand column of the second part of the form. To the sextant angle of 25° 35′ add the index error and, treating the monthly correction as optional, the sum from the table on page 86 in the almanac, or from figure 30 in this book. For a height of eye of 6 feet and an observed altitude of 26° (to the nearest whole degree) the correction is + 11.8′. This makes the true altitude 25° 47.9′: subtract this from 90° and the Observed Zenith Distance (O ZD) is 64° 12.1′.

Now turn to the left-hand column in part two of
the form. Start with the figure for GHA Sun at 0600:
the given figure for 0600 is 268° 28.4′, and for demon-
stration purposes the additions for 1 hour, 45 minutes
and 57 seconds are added separately; normally you get
the total for one hour and 45 minutes from the table
on page 88. The same table gives you 14.3′ as the
+ correction for 57 seconds. Add all these together
and you get the Sun GHA for 07.45.57 as 294° 57.7′.

To get the LHA from the GHA you have to either
add or subtract the DR longitude. Here you might use
the old saw for remembering how the sum goes. It is:

> 'Longitude West,
> Greenwich is Best.
> Longitude East,
> Greenwich is Least.'

In this case, with westerly longitude, you subtract
9° 30′ and get a (westerly) LHA of 285° 27.7′. Can you
remember from Chapter Eight what else we need to
find the CZD? We need the dead reckoning latitude
and the Sun's declination, which in this case is N 21°
00.2′.

You will see we have now got all the elements
required to obtain the CZD, and they are entered in the
left-hand column of part three. Look up the log versine
of the LHA and the log cosines of the latitude and
declination in the tables, enter them in the right-hand
column and add them together. Note that the second
figure before the decimal point is in brackets: we are
going to discard it straight away and only use the figure
nearest the decimal point. Find the total figure in the
log versine table by inspection – it is on page 195 and
falls between 9.6412 and 9.6414. By reading between
the figures in the adjacent column of natural versines
you find the exact equivalent is 0.4378, and this figure
is entered in the next space beneath the total figure.

Now we have to dart off at a tangent and deal with
the small sum in the centre of the third part of the
form. Here the latitude and the declination are compared to obtain a 'difference'. The rule is:

'Same names – Subtract,
Different names – Add.'

The latitude and declination both have a north prefix,
so you subtract and get a difference of 29° 14.8'. Enter
the natural versine columns with this angle and extract
the figure 0.1275 (page 192). Add this to the figure
immediately above it and you get a natural versine of
0.5653. The versine table shows you that (on page 197)
the angle equivalent to 0.5653 is either 64° 14' or
295° 46'. Common sense will tell you that CZD and
OZD will be fairly close together, so you discard the
latter angle and write in 64° 14' as the Calculated
Zenith Distance.

Naming the intercept completes the third part of the
form. Remember the mnemonic 'FOG' – 'From Observed Greater'. But here the CZD is larger than the
OZD, and the converse applies making the intercept
'Towards'. The sum at the left shows the intercept as
1.9 nautical miles 'towards'.

The last thing to do is to find the azimuth, or bearing,
of the heavenly body at the time the sight was taken.
The compass will give you this roughly, but that is not
good enough for our purposes and I suggest you use
the splendid short Time-Azimuth Table on page 175.
Detailed instructions are printed on the page facing it,
and the working is in the fourth part of the form. The
latitude and the LHA give a figure from Table A and
the LHA and declination from Table B. The sum or
difference gives a third figure which is used with the
latitude to get an angle from Table C. Naming the
azimuth may be a little tricky, but common sense will
tell you that a morning sun sight has the sun to the

eastward and that 088° T is about right for the sun's bearing at this hour of the morning.

The principal advantage of this method is that it can be used for any heavenly body at any time, in any part of the world. The second point is that you're working out of one book all the time, and don't have to wrestle with a number of volumes while the yacht is pitching

SIGHT FORM				
Date	Ht of Eye	Body Observed	Course	Log
D R Latitude		D R Longitude		G M T

GHA (two-hourly figure)   Sextant Angle
Correction (hr and mins)   Index Error
Correction (seconds)   Total Corr.
                    GHA   TRUE ALT
                    Longitude   90° 00.0'
                    LHA(W)   TRUE ALT
                    or LHA(E)   (OZD)

                    LHA   Log Versine
                    D R Lat   Log Cosine
                    Dec   Log Cosine
                                 Log Versine
                    Lat (+/-)   Nat Versine
                    Dec   +
OZD   = Nat Versine
CZD   Nat Versine
INTERCEPT Towards   CZD
           Away

D R Lat
LHA   Table A gives
Dec   Table B gives
                            Table C gives
           AZIMUTH =   or   °T

73   Figure 38

Turning
the tables

about in a seaway. End by trying the following example for yourself, using the blank sight form at figure 38.

On 30th June, while on passage from Malta to Gibraltar, you get the sextant angle of the sun's lower limb as 39° 25′ at 08.25.12 GMT. Your DR position is 35° 38′ N, 2° 11′ W, height of eye 10 feet, and no index error. Use figure 31 for data, and give the intercept and azimuth. *Answer page 116.*

10 *Position lines for a landfall*

'First the Dudgeon, then the Spurn;
Flambro' Head comes next in turn,
Flambro' Head as you pass by;
Filey Brigg is drawing nigh.
Scarbro' Castle stands out to sea,
And Whitby Light bears northerly.
Huntley Foot, that very high land,
Is twenty miles from Sunderland.
The Old Man says, "If things go right,
We'll be in Tyne tomorrow night . . ."
. . . Damn and Blast the Old Coal Trade!'
Traditional

This verse from the days of coastal sail demonstrates how the old-time collier skippers used landmarks to check progress and position. They were prime seamen, and to digress for a moment let me tell you about my favourite coal-trade character, who is still remembered with affection by senior 'flatiron' officers. He appears in the pages of his company's privately-printed history†
in the following passage. 'Captain James Lowrey, for instance, the master of *Ratcliff*, could neither read nor write. Notices to Mariners could have meant nothing at all to him. Yet he made hundreds of voyages between the North-East Coast ports and London with, as far as I can recollect, no major accident of any sort. When Captain Lowrey was over seventy years of age he was attacked at night by three toughs, who knew he was carrying the crew's wages: they were not quite tough enough, for two were taken to hospital and the third was found drowned in the dock on the following

† *William France Fenwick and Company Limited* 1954.

morning. The verdict was, of course, justifiable homi-
cide.'

Back to position lines and landfalls. The point I was
trying to make in the first sentence was that a distant
bearing of the land is still the finest check on position
of them all. After all, what yachtsman would sail from,
say, Whitby to the Elbe without sighting Heligoland,
or from Poole to Vigo without putting the yacht
firmly on the chart by reference to Ushant? The advantage of combining a position line obtained from the
sight of a heavenly body with a position line obtained
by the bearing compass is that your 'fix' can be plotted
the moment the landmark is identified: there is no
necessity to close the coast and obtain two compass
bearings to do so. I want to develop this theme in the
second half of the chapter; for the moment let me deal
with the single astronomical position line and the
various ways it can be used to help you reach a point
on the coast still far below the horizon.

The most obvious example has already been referred
to in chapters one and six – sailing along a parallel of

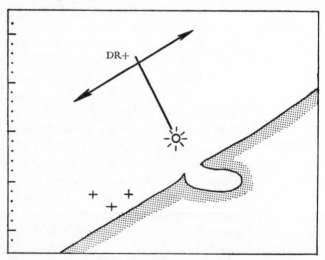

Figure 39

latitude to a point lying due east or west of your present position. The next instance is the single position line running parallel to an unseen coast, giving you the approximate distance-off for any point along that coast. In figure 39 a forenoon sun-sight gives such a position line, and the navigator can tell by reference to the scale at the side of his chart that he is some twelve miles off the land. Note here that I've started putting arrow heads on position lines: now that we're getting down to serious plotting you should know that posi-tion lines have single arrow heads and transferred position lines have double arrow heads. A dead reckoning position is marked with a cross, and a 'fix' with a circle: both have the time entered alongside.

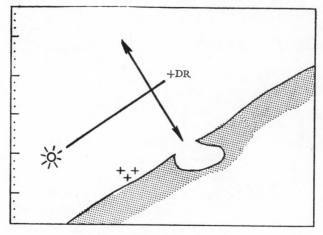

Figure 40

The single position line can also be helpful when it leads towards the shore. If you are sailing towards an unseen shore with the sun broad on the beam the position line can give you a true course to follow. In figure 40 the sun's azimuth runs from 055° T to 235° T, while the position line (on which the yacht must be) runs from 145° T to 325° T. By following a true course of 145° the yacht will come to an anchorage in the

sheltered bay still out of sight to the south-south-
eastward.

We can take this a step further. If your sight gives a
position line that does not lead to a harbour or estuary
at that time you can transfer the position line by dead
reckoning to a place on the chart where it will do some
good in the future. In figure 41 the navigator has got a

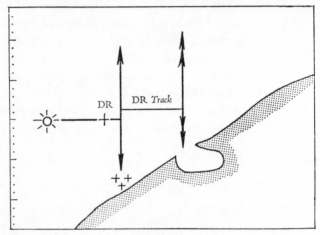

Figure 41

position line from an observation that leads towards a
dangerous part of the coast. By drawing in a transferred position line parallel to the original line and
leading into the bay the navigator can see that if he
alters course to 090° T, and sails for eight miles along
that course, he can get on the line and change course
to follow it to safety. This procedure would be
followed if, for instance, after you had obtained a
position line from a heavenly body a bank of fog
formed over the sea and prevented you taking any
further observations or bearings. That single position
line would be your only piece of data, and the safety
of the ship would depend on the way you used it.

Having introduced you to the transferred position
line let me run through an actual problem. Imagine

you are the navigator in a yacht approaching Mounts Bay from the south-westwards after a successful passage from the Azores. Your DR position is 49° 47′ N, 5° 29′ W, and at 1641 GMT the 9/10ths cloud cover parts long enough for you to get a snap altitude of the sun's lower limb. On working out the figures you find that the intercept is 3.1 miles 'away', and the azimuth is 262°. The log reading is 1319, and you are making about 4½ knots on a true course of 040°.

Look at figure 42. You begin by putting the DR position on the chart and drawing the azimuth through it. Mark off 3.1 miles 'away' with your dividers and draw in the position line at right angles. Stop for a moment and look at the position line. It could be quite useful by itself if you wanted to berth at Newlyn or Penzance, but for the purpose of this exercise I'll assume that Falmouth is the destination. This being the case the position line is not particularly helpful by itself for the moment. The yacht continues to forge ahead on a true course of 040°, and at 1731 GMT when the log shows 1323 you catch a glimpse of the Lizard to the north-eastward. The bearing compass comes out of its box in the doghouse, and you find the true bearing of the Lizard is 055°. You take a look at the chart and decide to get out of Mounts Bay and round the Lizard, leaving the latter about four miles to port to avoid the overfalls. What is your present position, and what is the true course the yacht should follow to leave the Lizard four miles on the port beam?

First plot the true bearing of the Lizard. Then, using dividers and the parallel ruler, mark off four miles in an 040° direction from the 1641 position line. Transfer the original position line carefully, and draw it in. (Figure 42 shows the transfer process by dotted lines.) The point where the transferred position line and the line of bearing of the Lizard intersect is the position of the yacht at 1731 GMT.

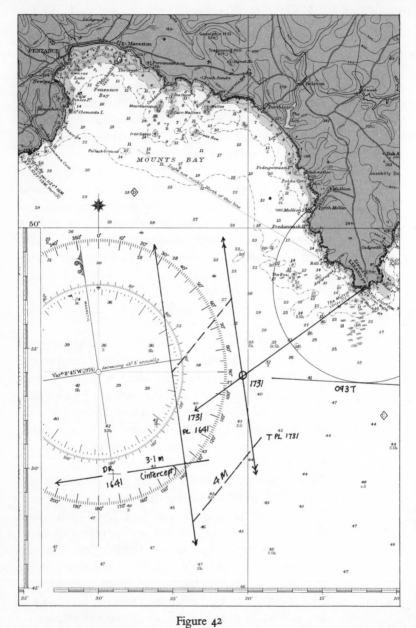

Figure 42

Reproduced from Admiralty Chart 2565 with the sanction of the Controller of
HM Stationery Office and the Hydrographer of the Navy.

With a point of the dividers (or pair of compasses) on the position of the Lizard lighthouse as marked on the chart, and a radius of four miles taken from the scale at the side of the chart, describe a half-circle. Draw a line from the 1731 'fix' position which just touches the half-circle south of the Lizard. Take your parallel ruler over to the compass rose and read off the figure: it will give you the true course to leave the Lizard four miles to port, which in this case is 093°. When the white octagonal tower that crowns Lizard Head bears true north it will be necessary to make another change of course to get the yacht round into Falmouth Bay and the Fal entrance.

I hope you'll agree that this has not been difficult. It is, after all, similar to the kind of plotting you would do on a coasting voyage. In the example there is a very short interval between getting the sun-sight position line and the land bearing, and a good angle of 'cut' at the intersection of the transferred position line and the line of bearing. A longer 'carry' of the original position line would not affect its subsequent validity, and a sun position line obtained at any time after about 1300 GMT would cross with the shore bearing in quite a satisfactory manner. It is only when the angle of 'cut' falls below 50° that accuracy diminishes significantly.

End by practising the transfer of position lines on an old chart. It will help you get into the way of using the dividers and parallel rulers confidently, and save you from making silly mistakes at sea. In the next two chapters we'll be using transferred position lines to obtain position when out of sight of land using only data obtained from sextant angles.

11 *Morning, noon and afternoon sights*

> 'I never used a sextant or worked an actual sight until I
> put to sea in *Svaap*. Then it was a case of sink or
> swim. I am a strong advocate of the principle that the
> only way to learn to do something is to get out and
> do it.'
>
> William Albert Robinson: *Deep Water and Shoal*

There are five times in a day when the navigator should
take the opportunity of fixing his position by reference
to heavenly bodies – even though he knows pretty
well where the yacht is by dead reckoning. At dawn
he should be out and about looking for a snap star
sight while the stars are clear in the sky and the horizon
shows as a hard line before the sun comes up. During
the morning he should be on hand to take a position
line sun-sight at any time after that body has risen to
more than 15° above the horizon. At noon the meridian altitude of the sun gives the latitude fairly painlessly,
and in the afternoon another sun-sight will give a
position line. At dusk he will again be alert for a star-
sight or a shot at Polaris for latitude. At dawn and dusk
the navigator will also want to take the bearing of the
rising or setting sun to check compass error.† Some
skippers follow the dubious practice of asking the navigator to double as cook. Don't do it: the navigator
will want to be out on deck when meals are being
prepared and should not be expected to serve two
masters. The cook is an important member of the crew:
so is the navigator. A cook/navigator is likely to come

† Described in the author's *Basic Coastal Navigation*: Adlard
Coles Ltd.

82

ashore very tired – having done more than his fair share during the voyage.

I want to leave star-sights for the next chapter and concentrate here on the trinity of sun-sights at mid-morning, noon and afternoon. The reasoning behind the figurework has already been covered in chapters six and nine, and as most of the remainder of this

SIGHT FORM

<u>Date</u>	<u>Ht of Eye</u>	<u>Body Observed</u>	<u>Course</u>	<u>Log</u>
16 June	6	LL Sun	185°T	321
	<u>D R Latitude</u>	<u>D R Longitude</u>	<u>G M T</u>	
	53° 50′ N	5° 15′ W	09.46.22	

	°	′		°	′
GHA (two-hourly figure)	299	51·6	Sextant Angle	47	47
Correction (hr and mins)	26	30·0	Index Error	NIL	
Correction (seconds)		5·5	Total Corr.	+12·9	
GHA	326	27·1	TRUE ALT	47	59·9
Longitude W	5	15·0		90°	00.0′
LHA(W)	321	12·1	TRUE ALT	47	59·9
or LHA(E)			(OZD)	42	00·1

		°	′		
LHA	W 321	12·1	Log Versine	9·3437	
D R Lat	N 53	50·0	Log Cosine	9·7710	
Dec	N 23	21·7	Log Cosine	9·9628	
			Log Versine (2)	9·0775	
Lat (+/-)	N 53	50·0	Nat Versine	0·1195	
Dec	N 23	21·7	+		
	30	28·3 =	Nat Versine	0·1381	
OZD 42 00·1			Nat Versine	0·2576	
CZD 42 04·0			CZD	42° 04′	
INTERCEPT 3·9 Towards ~~Away~~					

	°	′		
D R Lat N 53	50			
LHA W 321 12·1	Table A gives	+1·70		
Dec N 23 21·7	Table B gives	-0·689		
		+1·011	Table C gives	59·3

AZIMUTH = S 59° E or 121 °T

Figure 43

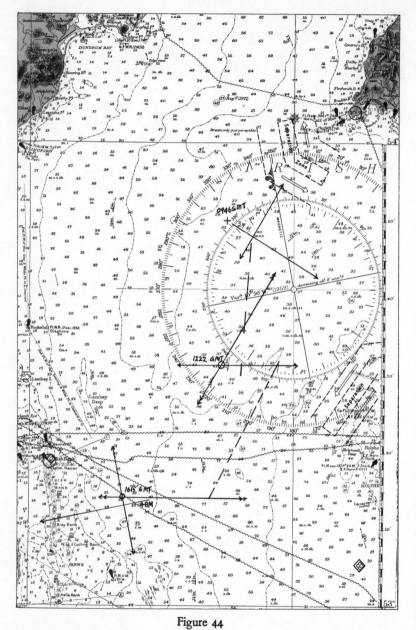

Figure 44

Reproduced from Admiralty Chart 1824A with the sanction of the Controller of
HM Stationery Office and the Hydrographer of the Navy.

chapter is taken up with a practical example I'll give the working without further explanation. Figures 43 and 45 cover the position line data while figure 44 gives the plotting of the day's programme of sun-sights.

This time our yacht is sailing in the Irish Sea, having left Port Erin at dawn on the 16th June, bound for Waterford. She's made a good offing from the land, and at about 1045 BST is in DR position 53° 50' N, 5° 15' W. At 09.46.22 GMT you get the angle of the sun's lower limb as 47° 47'. There is no index error, the height of eye is 6 feet and the log shows 321.0 on the dial. You fill in the sight form (figure 43) and come out with an intercept of 3.9' 'towards', and a true azimuth of 121°. Now look at figure 44. You put in the DR position at 0946 GMT (the nearest minute) and from it plot the line of azimuth. After marking off the intercept 3.9' 'towards' you draw in the position line at right angles and enter the time alongside. For the moment, that is that. There's no land in sight, and no other body available to get a 'fix'. The yacht stays on a compass course equivalent to 185° T.

The sun gets higher in the sky and swings round to the southward. Just before noon you look in the almanac for the time of the sun's meridian passage on the meridian of Greenwich and find it is 1201 GMT. The chart shows that you're still approximately in longitude 5° 15' W, and the sum to get the time of the sun meridian passage for that longitude goes as follows:

1201	GMT at Greenwich
+20	minutes for 5° W
+ 1	minute for 15' W
1222	GMT at 5° 15' W

In due course you get a sextant angle of 59° 37.4'.

The calculations can be made in the body of the log book, and the working is:

Corr. Observed Mer. Alt.   59° 37.4′ s (because sun bears southerly)

Total Corr. Table   + 12.9′ (includes monthly correction)

True Altitude   59° 50.3′ s

90° 00.0′
59° 50.3′ s

Zenith Distance   30° 09.7′ N (change of name)

Declination   23° 21.9′ N (from almanac)

LATITUDE   53° 31.6′

Draw in this position line from the scale at the side of the chart, and look at the log. It reads 332.5 – showing that you've sailed 11½ miles on a true course of 185° since you took the forenoon sun-sight. With dividers and the parallel ruler transfer the 0946 position line 11½ miles in a 185° direction, and mark it in. Where this transferred position line crosses the line of noon latitude is the position at 1222 GMT. Circle the intersection and put the time in beside it.

At this stage you should look carefully at the chart. The yacht is bang in the middle of the Irish Sea and it would be logical to edge over a bit towards the Irish coast. The obvious point to aim for is the Codling Light Vessel in latitude 53° 03′ N, 5° 41′ W, for it'll provide a check on position while keeping the ship clear of the shoal water extending well offshore on this coast. The true course to follow to sight the Codling is 208°, and the yacht should be put on the appropriate compass course to head in that direction.

Time passes, and a little after 1700 BST the sun has come round nicely for an afternoon position line sight. You get everything ready; check the sextant for index error, and at 16.14.30 GMT get an angle of 37° 25′ on the instrument. The log reading is 352.0, the height of eye is 6 feet and the sextant has +0.5′ of index error. This time there are two ways of finding the DR position: by plotting and by a Traverse Table, and I'll deal with plotting first. You plot the DR position by laying the ruler along the line of the true course from the previous 'fix', marking off the number of miles covered according to the log. In this case it is 352 − 332.5 = 19½ miles, and the new DR position is 53° 14′ N, 5° 31′ W. You complete the sight form (figure 45) and extract an intercept of 4.8′ 'towards' and a true azimuth of 259°. You draw in the azimuth from the DR position, mark off the intercept, put in the position line at right angles, and transfer the noon line of latitude to pass through the DR position. The intersection of the two lines is your position at 1615 GMT.

Plotting a DR position in this way is easy enough when all the work is on one chart, but with a long 'carry' of the transferred noon position line or where you have to start plotting on another chart I suggest you use the traverse table found on pages 210–13 in *Reed's Nautical Almanac*. It has several uses, but in this context we use it to get the new DR position without reference to the chart, using only the previous latitude and longitude, the true course and the distance covered.

In our example the noon observation established the position of the yacht at 1222 GMT as 53° 31.6′ N, 5° 16.8′ W. It then sails 208° T for 19½ miles. Now, to use the traverse table to get the DR position we have to re-duce this true course of 208° to manageable proportions, and we do this by changing the notation. 208° can also be expressed as N 152° w or s 28° w, and we use this last-named figure because the table only caters for angles from 0° to 90°. You enter the table on page 211 with 28° at the left-hand side and between the 19' and 20' columns at the top of the page. By interpolation the figure for Difference of Latitude (D.Lat.)

SIGHT FORM

Date	Ht of Eye	Body Observed	Course	Log
16 June	6	LL Sun	207° T	352
D R Latitude		D R Longitude		G M T
53° 14' N		5° 31' W		16 . 14 . 30

	°	'		°	'
GHA (two-hourly figure)	59	50·5	Sextant Angle	37	25·0
Correction (hr and mins)	3	30·0	Index Error		+00·5
Correction (seconds)		7·5	Total Corr.		+12·3
GHA	63	28·0	TRUE ALT	37	37·8
Longitude W	5	31·0		90°	00.0'
LHA(W)	57	57	TRUE ALT	37	37·8
or LHA(E)			(OZD)	52	22·2

		°	'		
LHA W	57	57·0	Log Versine		9 ·6715
D R Lat N	53	14·0	Log Cosine		9·7771
Dec N	23	22·2	Log Cosine		9·9628
			Log Versine (2)		9·4114
Lat (+/-) N	53	14·0	Nat Versine		0·2578
Dec N	23	22·2	+		
	29	51·8 =	Nat Versine		0·1328
			Nat Versine		0·3906
			CZD		52° 27'

OZD 52 22·2
CZD 52 27·0
INTERCEPT 4·8 ~~Towards~~ Away

	°	'		
D R Lat N	53	14	Table A gives	+0·838
LHA W	57	57	Table B gives	-0·516
Dec N	23	22·2		+0·322
			Table C gives	79·1

AZIMUTH = S 79° W or 259 °T

Figure 45

is 17.3′, and that for Departure (Dep.) is 9.2′. You deal
with the latitude first, and the sum goes:

Latitude left   53° 31.6′ N
     D. Lat.   − 17.3′ s (from notation)
—————————
Latitude in   = 53° 14.3′ N
—————————

For the Difference of Longitude (D. Long.) you have
to take the 9.2′ Departure figure to the table on page
208. You enter this table with 53° 20′ (the mean, or
average, latitude from the sum above), and interpolate
for 9.2′ between the '9' and '10' columns, getting a difference of longitude of 15.4′ which is applied as follows:

Longitude left   5° 16.8′ w
     D. Long.   + 15.4′ w (from notation)
—————————
Longitude in =   5° 32.2′ w
—————————

– which gives you a latitude and longitude very close
to the DR position you obtained by plotting.

To round off this example look again at figure 44.
The 1615 'fix' tells you that wind, tide or current, has
been pushing the yacht to the westward during the
afternoon, and it would be common sense to alter
course to about 196° T to pass between the line of buoys
marking the shoals and the light-vessel, for within an
hour you should be able to ascertain position by cross-
bearings. The tide would have to enter into your
calculations from this point forward and would dictate
whether you would hug the coast or stand offshore
during the evening. The rest of your voyage down to
the Tuskar and round to Waterford is a matter of
coastal pilotage: the sun-sights have guided you
through the central forty miles of the passage and have
given you sure knowledge of the position, and peace
of mind, throughout the day.

12   *The stars above*

'And when neither sun nor stars in many days appeared,
and no small tempest lay on us, all hope that we should
be saved was then taken away.'
Acts 27: 20 – the shipwreck of St Paul

A change of weather frequently occurs during morning
or evening twilight, and a lull at this time may bring
a brief band of clear sky to divide overcast day from
cloudy night. This is when star-sights come into their
own – particularly if the sun has not been visible for a
couple of days and you are uncertain of your position.
The problem is twofold: identification of the star or
stars themselves, and the figurework and plotting the
position lines.

Star recognition should be practised during the
winter months when yachts lie in their mud berths and
navigators have leisure to study the sky. About 4,850
stars are visible in the heavens, and about 170 of these
are of navigational interest. The amateur seaman will
find that about 40 are useful – provided always that he
can recognize them for what they are. My view is that
there are 15 stars that can be identified from small
vessels in any weather, and they appear in figure 46.
Look at the illustration and follow me through the next
paragraph.

In the northern hemisphere the stars appear to re-
volve around Polaris anti-clockwise, and you'll remember from chapter seven that Polaris is found by
reference to the Plough which dominates the northern
sky. Three stars in the Plough can be useful to the
navigator. Dubhe – the 'pointer' nearest to Polaris,
Benetnasch at the extreme end of the 'handle' of the

Plough, and Alioth, next but one to Benetnasch. The
continuation of the 'handle' leads to Arcturus – an
orange-coloured star, and the sixth brightest in the
heavens. The constellation Cassiopeia has a charac-
teristic 'W' or 'M' shape, and is always to be found on
the opposite side of Polaris from the Plough. The top
left peak of the 'M', or bottom right trough of the

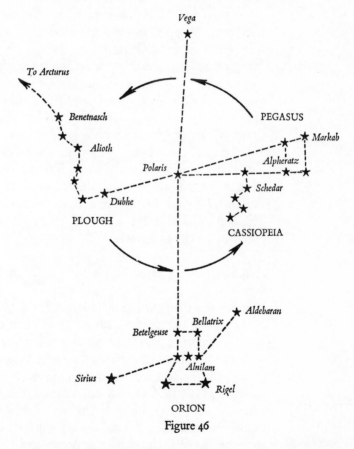

Figure 46

'W' – depending on how you look at it, is Schedar –
brightest of the five stars in Cassiopeia. An imaginary
line joining Dubhe, Polaris and the last star in

Cassiopeia brings you to the Square of Pegasus with Markab as the back-marker and Alpheratz in the opposite corner nearest Polaris. At right angles to this Plough–Polaris–Cassiopeia–Pegasus axis is the Orion group of stars with Betelgeuse and Bellatrix nearest Polaris. Rigel occupies the south-east corner and Alnilam is the centre of three stars forming the 'belt' of Orion. The line of the 'belt' gives the position of Sirius to the south-west and Aldebaran somewhat off-centre to the north-east. Vega sits in solitary splendour on the other side of Polaris from Orion.

Figure 46 is not drawn to scale, but it may help you to grasp the relationship of stars one to another and give you a good 'spread' of identifiable stars for the purposes of navigation. The position line from star sights is obtained in almost the same way as the sun position line, there being only two major differences. The first is that you have to use a different correction table to get true altitude, and this is found on page 87 in *Reed's Nautical Almanac*, or in figure 30 in this book. The second is that the Local Hour Angle (LHA) is obtained by the formula:

$$\text{LHA Star} = \text{GHA Aries} + \text{SHA Star} \begin{array}{c} + \text{ east} \\ - \text{ west} \end{array} \text{longitude.}$$

In practice this calculation is included in the working of the second part of the standard sight form used for sun position lines. Figure 47 shows a practical example with a sight form adapted for a star sight. Imagine that during the evening of the 15th July, your yacht is under way in the western entrance of the English Channel in DR position 49° 02′ N, 5° 07.5′ W. No sights have been taken for 36 hours, but during evening twilight the sky clears to the north and east long enough for you to get the sextant angle of Vega as 61° 20.9′. The GMT at the time of taking the sight is 20.50.00, the height of eye 6 feet, and the index error is nil. At the same time the sextant angle of Polaris was 48° 22.5′. What is your present position?

The only part of figure 47 I want to comment on is

SIGHT FORM

Date	Ht of Eye	Body Observed	Course	Log
15 July	6	VEGA	277°T	98

D R Latitude	D R Longitude	G M T
49° 02′ N	5° 07·5′W	20·50·00

GHA (two-hourly figure) **ARIES** 233 43·7 Sextant Angle 61 20·9

Correction (hr and mins) **ARIES** 12 32·1 Index Error   NIL

Correction (seconds) **SHA VEGA** 81 01·6 Total Corr.   −02·9

GHA 327 17·4 TRUE ALT 61 18

Longitude W 5 07·5   90° 00.0′

LHA(W) 322 09·9 TRUE ALT 61 18·0

or LHA(E)   (OZD) 28 42·0

LHA W 322 09·9 Log Versine 9·3226

D R Lat N 49 02·0 Log Cosine 9·8167

Dec N 38 45·2 Log Cosine 9·8920

Log Versine (2) 9·0313

Lat (+/−) N 49 02·0 Nat Versine 0·1074

Dec N 38 45·2 +

OZD 28 42·0   10 16·8 = Nat Versine 0·0161

CZD 28 46·5   Nat Versine 0·1235

INTERCEPT 4·5 Towards   CZD 28° 46·5′

D R Lat N 49 02

LHA W 322 09·9 Table A gives + 1·49

Dec N 38 45·2 Table B gives − 1·34

+ 0·15   Table C gives 84·4

AZIMUTH = S 84° E or 096 °T

Figure 47

that part of section two leading up to the angle of LHA Star. There are two ways of getting LHA, and on the form I've used the GHA Aries method. The alternative

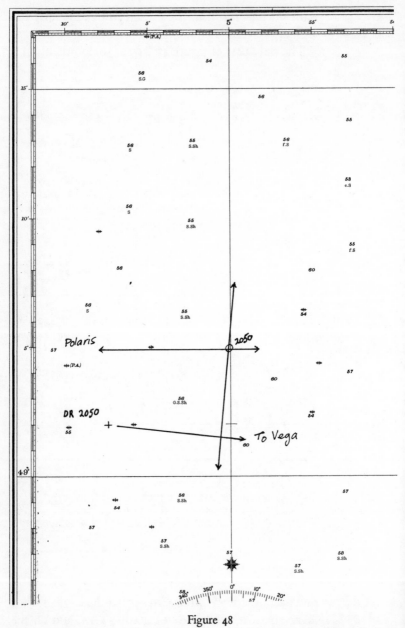

Figure 48

Reproduced from Admiralty Chart 2644 with the sanction of the Controller of
HM Stationery Office and the Hydrographer of the Navy.

is to start the sum with the GHA of the star, and this way of working is put in here for comparison purposes. An explanation as to where the data can be found is given below.

Working

1st July   GHA Vega at 0 hours   =   0° 08.1'
                                        Second monthly page in *Reed's*.
15th July + Correction for date   =   13° 48.0'
                                        Page 89; top column 1.
          + Corr. for 20 hours   =   300° 49.3'
                                        Page 89; bottom col. 1.
          + Corr. for 50 mins.   =   12° 32.1'
                                        Page 89; column 3.

15th July   GHA Vega at 2050   327° 17.5'

            Longitude west   5° 07.5' −

            LHA Vega (W)   322° 10.0'

            LHA Vega (E)   37° 50.0'

The sight eventually gives you an intercept of 4.5' 'towards' and a true azimuth of 096°.

Before we pass on a few words about Vega may not come amiss. This interesting star is bluish in colour, and its name derives from the Arabic – 'Al-waki', meaning 'the descending one' (i.e. vulture). The fourth brightest star in the heavens, it has an interesting future, for, due to the wobble of the earth on its axis Vega will be the Pole Star in AD 14,000.

However, back to the problem in hand. Figure 48 gives the plotting of this position line which is crossed with the parallel of latitude obtained from the Polaris sight. The working of the latter is as follows:

GHA Aries at 2000 GMT on 15th July = 233° 43.7′
Correction for 50 mins. = 12° 32.1′
_____

GHA Aries at 2050 GMT = 246° 15.8′
Longitude west (−) = 5° 07.5′
_____

LHA Aries   241° 08.3′
_____

Observed alt. Polaris   48° 22.5′
Star total correction   − 3.3′
_____

True altitude   48° 19.2′
_____

Pole Star corr. table for 1968   + 45.7′
_____

LATITUDE   49° 04.9′
_____

When the sky is clear it is usual to take three star angles as quickly as possible and plot them as if they were taken simultaneously. The intersection of the three position lines usually makes a small triangle – as in figure 49, and the position of the yacht is then deemed to be the centre of that triangle. A sailing yacht does not travel far in, say, five minutes, but if there is any appreciable interval between sights you will have to carry the first, and perhaps the second, position lines forward by the distance shown on the log. It's a good idea to get another crew member to read the sextant after getting each angle, and to ask him to write it down for you. This way vision is not affected by your having to peer at the arc in artificial light prior to focusing again on a distant star through the telescope.

Planets need very little comment. Data for Venus, Mars, Jupiter and Saturn is given on every fifth monthly page in *Reed's Nautical Almanac*. Planets are not 'fixed' like stars, and there can be identification difficulties,

particularly with Mars which is sometimes rather dim
and distant and can be confused with Antares because
both have a reddish tinge. You will see from the almanac that at some times they are too close to the sun to be

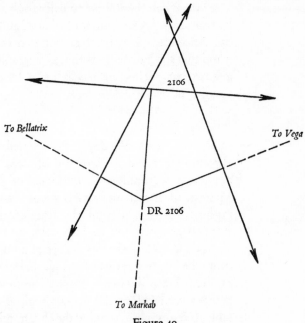

To Bellatrix

To Vega

2106

DR 2106

To Markab

Figure 49

of any use, and of course they cannot be used when
much below 15° of altitude. Note that you must em-
ploy the special correction tables for the declination and
GHA of planets on pages 156–60 in the almanac. In the
early stages I suggest you take two star sights to each
planet sight: the size of the position triangle will tell
you if you're working along the right lines.

97

13   *What's the time?*

'... but, when the Rabbit actually took a watch out of its waistcoat-pocket, and looked at it, and then hurried on, Alice started to her feet, for it flashed across her mind that she had never before seen a rabbit with either a waistcoat-pocket, or a watch to take out of it....'
Lewis Carroll

In the bad, bad, old days ships carried two or three chronometers and a drawerful of deck watches, but navigators were still never quite sure of the exact time. Masters of merchant vessels awoke sweating from nightmares in which all the timepieces in the ship stopped at once, for to lose GMT meant an end to accurate navigation. On voyages of a hundred days or more the loss of GMT was a serious matter, and an elaborate ritual was devised whereby the steward placed a printed card before the captain's place at the saloon table to remind him to wind the chronometers immediately after breakfast each morning. The chronometers were gimballed and wound a precise number of turns each day with a gentle even motion. They could not stand up to robust treatment, and were kept cradled and cushioned in the master's cabin. Deck watches were used when taking sights and compared with the chronometers later to get the GMT. Nervous captains would heave-to in mid-ocean and row across to passing vessels to compare chronometers, while each individual instrument was compared daily with its sisters to try to eliminate error due to vibration and temperature changes. This state of affairs came to an end with the advent of radio time signals, and ports sporting tall masts from which time balls were dropped precisely at noon to give GMT to the ships in harbour converted them to supports for seaside illuminations. Page 826 of *Reed's Nautical Almanac* gives a list of radio time signals available to navigators in home waters, and Volume Five of the *Admiralty List of Radio Signals* has details of facilities available in other parts of the world.

In recent years the marine chronometer has been improved to the point where error is reduced to a minimum. Bulova Ltd make a modern yacht chronometer with three separate timekeeping units and powered by a mercury-oxide battery which lasts for a whole year. This instrument has a maximum anticipated error of two seconds a day, although in a recent ocean race one of these chronometers varied only one second between Bermuda and Copenhagen. The short-range navigator can get along very well with a good wrist-watch, for developments in the watch industry in the last few years have made the acquisition of GMT a simple matter for the yachtsman. The modern watch has up to 36,000 beats a minute, a self-winding mechanism, and is based on new concepts such as the regularity of tuning-fork vibrations rather than on the gradual unwinding of a coiled steel spring. The fast beat of these new watches cuts out error due to movement, changes of position and fluctuating temperatures, while further research is going on to explore the time-keeping properties of quartz crystals and caesium atoms. It is confidently predicted that in the foreseeable future a wrist chronometer will be developed with a maximum error of one second in 3,000 years!

Chronometers and watches should not be corrected from day to day to correspond exactly with the GMT obtained from a radio time signal: it is better practice to note the error, fast or slow, in the log and then apply a small correction to get the GMT for each sight.

This recording of the rate of error has value if the
radio receiver stops working, for you have a note of
each day's error and can make future calculations
on the basis of the past rate of change noted in the
log.

Your chronometer, or watch, is kept on GMT all the
time – irrespective of the position of the yacht on the
surface of the earth. So that there shall be no bickering
over the length of watches, and the times of meals, it is
advisable to set the cabin clock to local time. This is
done according to the time zone of your present
position, and a useful diagram is given on page 94 in
Reed's Nautical Almanac. Zone Time is an arbitrary
slicing-up of the hours dependent on whether you are
east or west of Greenwich, and from $7\frac{1}{2}°$ E longitude
to $7\frac{1}{2}°$ W longitude you are in Zone 0 where local time
is the same as BST. From $7\frac{1}{2}°$ W to $22\frac{1}{2}°$ W you are in
Zone + 1, and from $22\frac{1}{2}°$ W to $37\frac{1}{2}°$ W in Zone + 2,
and so on. In these zones you are 1 and 2 hours slow of
GMT, while in minus zones to the east of Greenwich
the clock is advanced by the appropriate amount. I
suggest that you don't make adjustments of a whole
hour when changing zones but alter the clock day by
day at a fixed hour, such as midnight, so that the
watches which the crew belong to gain, or lose, a small
amount of time in turn. The difference in longitude
will indicate the rate of change for each 24 hours
according to the following table:

$$15° \text{ of longitude} = \text{one hour}$$
$$1° \text{ of longitude} = \text{four minutes}$$
$$15' \text{ of longitude} = \text{one minute}$$
$$1' \text{ of longitude} = \text{four seconds}$$

thus, the navigator of a sailing yacht going west across
the Atlantic should put the cabin clock back about ten
minutes every day.

The politicians have been changing their minds in the last few years about land clock time, and briefly introduced, and then did away with, British Standard Time. We are now back to the pre-1968 position and use GMT in winter and British Summer Time – GMT plus one hour – in the summer months. There is no change in the use of GMT for navigational purposes. In adjacent European countries Central European Time will be in force, and this will correspond with British Summer Time. Outside Western Europe the cabin clock may have to be changed when you are in port to square up with the local time ashore, for governments are prone to fix time in a rather arbitrary manner that does not conform to zone time. A cruise from Southern Italy to Greece brings a one hour change, as does the short crossing from Moroccan ports to Gibraltar. It's worse in South America. Uruguay and Paraguay lie cheek by jowl but have an hour's difference, while Guyana and French Guiana manage to stagger their civil times three-quarters of an hour apart. A full list of standard times appears on pages 10 and 11 in *Reed's Nautical Almanac*, but you should always enquire ashore about any variation due to the time of the year, the whim of the government, or the success or failure of the last revolution.

The Greenwich date – referred to in chapter eight – may also give you trouble. An error of a whole day is a serious business, and if you're a long way east or west of Greenwich you must work out the Greenwich date before entering the tables. Look at the following example.

At sea in longitude 130° w (Zone +9) on the 19th July, you take an observation of the sun's lower limb during the afternoon when the cabin clock says half past four and the chronometer gives the GMT as 01.30. 20. What is the Greenwich date?

Set out your working as follows:

Approximate zone time	1630
Zone	+ 0900
Approximate GMT	2530
Subtract for whole of 19th July	2530
	− 2400
Approximate GMT for 20th July =	0130

so, you enter the tables with 01.31.20 GMT on 20th July.

Finally, you may need a timepiece for very short periods of time. A stop-watch is a necessity for racing starts and can be very useful when taking sights single-handed. Hold the stop-watch in the left hand and start it going at the moment of getting the angle. The reading can be compared with the chronometer when you get below and start working at the chart table.

14 *Plotting and planning*

Judge: 'I perceive that this case relates to the repair of a pleasure yacht. May I have the definition of a yacht?'
Counsel: 'According to the plaintiff, m'lud, a yacht is a hole in the water completely surrounded by wood, into which he pours money!'

It will be appreciated that on a long voyage you'll get beyond the range of coastal charts in a couple of days and will then be faced with the problem of finding something suitable for doing the plotting on. Plain paper, or a blank page in the log-book, will sometimes do, but you will have to put in a rudimentary scale for latitude and longitude and draw in at least one parallel of latitude and one meridian of longitude to ensure getting the DR position in the right place. If you know approximately what area of sea your yacht will be traversing you might like to copy my dodge of cutting a compass rose and scales from an old chart of the right latitude, sticking them on plain paper, and using a photo-copier to produce foolscap-sized plotting sheets that can be discarded after use.

Squared paper can also be used for plotting position lines, but you must be careful about scale. A degree of longitude is 60 miles from east to west at the equator, but gets smaller as you move away north or south from the equator. In the latitude of the English Channel it is about 39 miles in length, and at 60° N is only 30 miles long. Most charts are based on Mercator's projection where the meridians are drawn parallel to each other and the latitude scale is 'stretched' to prevent distortion. This accounts for the fact that scales of degrees and minutes at the top and bottom of a chart do not

correspond with nautical miles – except at the equator
– and why we take distances with the dividers from
that part of the latitude scale abreast of our present
position. If the intercepts are small no great harm will
be done by plotting on blank squared paper, but if they
cover a lot of sea it will be necessary to mark off, for
example, sixty squares northward for a degree of
latitude and forty westward for a degree of longitude.
The following rough table will be of some assistance:

In latitude 45° a degree of longitude is 42½ miles in length

,,	,,	47°	,,	,,	41	,,	,,
,,	,,	49°	,,	,,	39½	,,	,,
,,	,,	51°	,,	,,	38	,,	,,
,,	,,	52°	,,	,,	37	,,	,,
,,	,,	55°	,,	,,	34½	,,	,·
,,	,,	59°	,,	,,	31	,,	,,
,,	,,	60°	,,	,,	30	,,	,,

Another alternative is to use the Plotting Table
Diagram (5004C) obtainable from Admiralty chart
agents at a few pence. This is a blank chart with a large
central compass rose and a latitude scale without
figures at the right-hand edge. 5004C is simple to use: I
always put the DR position at the centre of the compass
rose and pencil in the scales to match it. The big advantage with 5004C is that you can use it day after day,
rubbing off the previous day's work each morning.

When planning a long ocean crossing you must first
consult that admirable publication *Ocean Passages for
the World*. This book will tell you all about prevailing
winds, currents and weather conditions, as well as
underlining the dangers of the West Indian hurricane
season or the perils of Sumatras and typhoons. When
you've decided that the crossing is feasible in terms of
expected weather you must run through every part of
a complicated equation based on estimated speed,
distance and weight of stores and water to see if the

vessel can make it without being unduly overloaded. Finally, you can work out the course to your destination.

It would be natural to assume that the way to get the true track of the voyage would be to go out and buy a small-scale ocean chart, draw in a straight line joining the starting point to the destination, and try and follow that line as closely as possible. Well, what you've drawn is a rhumb line course, which is one way of getting to the destination, but not the shortest way there. Let me explain why. Charts drawn to Mercator's projection have been distorted to keep the meridians parallel to each other, and a track line cuts them all at the same angle. The 'real' straight line on the surface

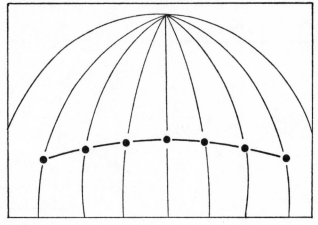

Figure 50

of a sphere can best be demonstrated by imagining that you have an old-fashioned wooden globe of the world, and stick two drawing pins in it to mark two cities which have a difference of longitude of 120°. (See figure 50.) Stretch a piece of cotton tightly between the pins, and make it fast at both ends. Note that the cotton has naturally taken up the curve of the shortest route between the pins, and that it is, in fact, part of a great circle. Stick in a row of smaller pins along the cotton, placing one at every 20° meridian of longitude – as in figure 50. You can see without measuring that the angle that the cotton makes with each meridian changes slightly as you go east or west, and is the 'real' straight line on a sphere. In practice we make that curve a series of lesser straight lines (or true courses) from one 5° meridian to the next, so that the yacht is not continually making minute alterations of course to stick to the great circle track.

To get these portions of the true track the navigator turns to a special chart where the meridians converge and the parallels of latitude appear as curved lines. A

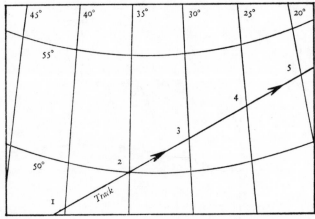

Figure 51

gnomonic chart is based on a projection that ensures that any straight line drawn on it is equivalent to part of a great circle, and for the North Atlantic you would need number 5095, which costs under a pound. Once you have drawn the straight line from your present position to the destination you only have to make a note of the latitude where that line crosses each 5° meridian. Figure 51 shows part of a gnomonic chart

with a track line on it: the approximate required
position for each 5° of longitude is:

1	2	3	4	5
48° 35′ N	50° 00′ N	51° 55′ N	52° 30′ N	53° 20′ N
40° 00′ W	35° 00′ W	30° 00′ W	25° 00′ W	20° 00′ W

These positions can be transferred to a chart based on
Mercator's projection if you wish, but in mid-ocean it
will usually suffice to have a note of them in the log-
book. The small-scale ocean chart mentioned earlier
can be pinned to a bulkhead and the noon position
entered every day so that the crew can see what progress is being made. Of course, no sailing yacht could
follow a great circle track exactly, and if the wind
comes ahead you must choose a course that does not
depart too far from the great circle. In such cases you
could plot the great circle track and the rhumb line
track on a chart and select some intermediate course to
suit wind direction and prevailing weather conditions.

One last word. Great circle sailing is most advan-
tageous in high latitudes and where the mean course is
east or west. If bound near enough to the north or
south you can make your calculations on an ordinary
chart, as you can when sailing close to the equator.
Quite often the great circle track will run over land or
shoals, and part of the voyage is based on the great
circle track, and part on the rhumb line. In some cases,
too, the great circle track takes you into too high a
latitude and you have to draw up a course which is
partly great circles and partly sailing along a maximum
parallel of latitude. This is called composite great circle
sailing: it can be tricky and is best left to professional
navigators.

15   *On the coast*

'Oh, 'e fished all one night off the Haisbro' Bank,
and 'e caught twenty stone – but the ruddy boat sank!
still I love 'im: I'll fergive 'im,
I'll go wiv 'im –wherever 'e goes.'
Traditional: The Black Shawl

The sextant has the edge over the bearing compass for accuracy in coastal work, and can be of great assistance in providing the navigator with distance, direction and position. The first use of the sextant in this context is in giving the horizontal danger angle from shoremarks.

Imagine that you are sailing along parallel to the coast and have to get round a headland with a dangerous reef extending from it. Your aim would be to pass the reef at a safe distance, but not to sail so far offshore that you lose a lot of time through excessive caution. The sextant can give you the safe and economical course to steer; look at figure 52 and follow the reasoning. 'A' and 'B' are beacons on the shore on each side of the headland, and 'C' is a point two cables clear of the reef where your yacht can pass the dangerous point in safety. Draw a circle on the chart which passes through 'A', 'B' and 'C', and join 'A' to 'C' and 'B' to 'C' with straight lines. Measure the angle at 'C' with the protractor – you'll find it's about 53°. Note here that all angles in the same segment of a circle are equal, and that any lines from 'A' and 'B' meeting on the seaward side of the circle will make the same angle. 'X' and 'Y' are put in to demonstrate this point.

As you sail along towards 'Z' set 53° on the arc of your sextant and train it horizontally on 'A' and 'B' with the mirrors uppermost. At first the angle will be acute, but as you get closer to 'Z' it will broaden out until at 'Z' the two beacons cover each other in the horizon mirror and you know that the angle between 'A' and 'B' is 53°. This is your cue to stand off the land and follow the arc round to 'M' by reference to the sextant angle. As long as it does not exceed 53° you will know that you're on a safe course. This kind of observation is best made from the foredeck where you have a clear field of view, and the helmsman can be given verbal instructions to stand on, or off, the land while you concentrate on the horizontal angle. After passing 'M' your common sense will tell you that as 'B' is nearly right ahead it's time you set a fresh course to steer along the land again.

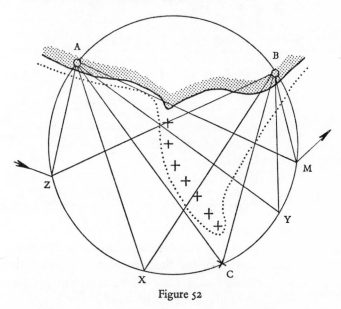

Figure 52

The sextant and bearing compass can be used together to establish position where the angle is acute and there are obvious difficulties in measuring distant objects by the bearing compass alone. Greater accuracy will be achieved by measuring the angle between two shoremarks by the sextant and taking the compass bearing of the nearest mark at the same time. In figure 53 the line of bearing runs to a beacon at 'A', and the horizontal sextant angle between 'A' and 'B' – 15° – is marked in at any point on the line of bearing. Transfer the line representing the sextant angle by parallel ruler until it cuts the beacon at 'B', and draw it in. The intersection of this transferred line with the line of the compass bearing is the position of the yacht at the time of taking the angle.

Vertical sextant angles of prominent shoremarks, such as lighthouses, will give the distance from the mark by use of a table on pages 241–44 in *Reed's Nautical Almanac*,

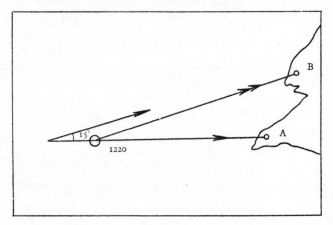

Figure 53

and the same procedure ensures safe passage past off-shore dangers when coasting. The vertical danger angle is taken in virtually the same way as the angle of heavenly bodies: the chief difference being that you treat the line of foam where land and sea meet as the horizon. One word of caution about lighthouses. Their heights, as given on the chart or in the almanac, refer to the centre of the lantern – not the topmost part of the structure of the lighthouse. By entering the table with the height and the sextant reading you obtain the distance-off: by entering with the height and the proposed distance-off you get the safety angle. Figure 54 shows the use of this table.

In the example an observer in a yacht wishes to sail his ship four cables clear of a submerged rock which stands seven cables off-shore from a lighthouse whose lantern is 350 feet above sea level.

Page 248 in *Reed's Nautical Almanac* contains the column for 350 feet, and by looking down it to where 1 mile, 1 cable (the distance-off) appears in either margin you can see that the safety angle is 3° 00′. Set this on your sextant: if the angle from lantern to the base of the cliff grows to be greater than 3° you will know

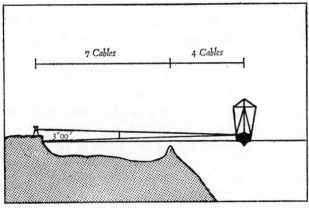

Figure 54

that you're too close and must stand off the shore. The charted heights of these shore objects are calculated from high-water mark and the height of the observer's eye above sea level is ignored. This gives an additional margin of safety and ensures that you will usually be further away from the danger than the table indicates. If you want to fix your position while rounding a dangerous part of the coast this is done by crossing the safety arc obtained by vertical sextant angle with a compass bearing. Figure 55 shows a 'fix' obtained in this way.

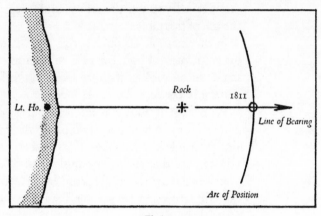

Rock

Lt. Ho.

1811

Line of Bearing

Arc of Position

Figure 55

I like to think of these vertical sextant angles as a kind of poor man's radar, for by taking the two angles of charted objects one after the other you get an excellent 'fix'. In figure 56 a yacht is passing between two rocky islands: the larger is 1,500 feet high, and the smaller 850 feet. The vertical sextant angle of the larger island from surf to peak is 2° 14′, and that of the smaller island is 2° 00′. By entering the distance-off table with

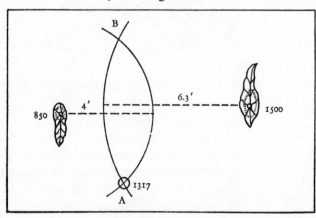

B

850

4′

6.3′

1500

1317

A

Figure 56

the heights and angles you get a range of 6.3 miles for the larger island and 4 miles for the smaller. Set these distances on a pair of compasses from the latitude scale, put the point on each peak in turn, and describe two arcs. They intersect twice, at 'A' and 'B'. Normally you know whether you are north or south of a line joining the two islands, and can eliminate the 'fix' that does not apply. If in doubt the compass bearing of the nearer island will settle the issue.

One last tip. If you haven't got any tables with you the following rule will give the distance-off.

MULTIPLY THE HEIGHT BY 0.565 AND DIVIDE THE RESULT BY THE SEXTANT ANGLE IN MINUTES.

Example: Cape Barfleur lighthouse has a charted height of 236 feet, and its vertical sextant angle is 30′. What is the distance-off?

```
   236                        4.44
     0.565            30′ ) 133.34
  ------                   120
                           ---
   1.180
  14.16                     133
 118.0                      120
                            ---
  ------
 133.340                    134
  ------                    120
                            ---
```

The distance-off is therefore 4.4 miles.

Table I

JUNE
(30 days)

G.M.T.

Date Yr.	Mth.	Day of Week.	Equation of Time — Add/Sub. from M. Time 0h (m. s.)	Equation of Time 12h (m. s.)	⊙ Transit (h. m.)	⊙ Semi diam	SUN Lat. 52°N. Twi-light (h. m.)	Sun-rise	Sun-set	Twi-light
152	1	Sun	+02 22	+02 18	11 58	15·8	3 00	3 46	20 10	20 57
153	2	M	+02 13	+02 09	11 58	15·8	2 59	3 45	20 11	20 58
154	3	Tu	+02 04	+01 59	11 58	15·8	2 58	3 45	20 12	20 59
155	4	W	+01 54	+01 49	11 58	15·8	2 57	3 44	20 13	21 00
156	5	Th	+01 44	+01 39	11 58	15·8	2 56	3 43	20 14	21 01
157	6	F	+01 34	+01 28	11 59	15·8	2 55	3 43	20 15	21 03
158	7	s	+01 23	+01 17	11 59	15·8	2 54	3 42	20 16	21 04
159	8	Sun	+01 12	+01 06	11 59	15·8	2 54	3 42	20 17	21 05
160	9	M	+01 00	+00 54	11 59	15·8	2 53	3 41	20 17	21 06
161	10	Tu	+00 48	+00 42	11 59	15·8	2 52	3 41	20 18	21 07
162	11	W	+00 36	+00 30	12 00	15·8	2 52	3 41	20 19	21 08
163	12	Th	+00 24	+00 18	12 00	15·8	2 51	3 40	20 19	21 08
164	13	F	+00 12	+00 05	12 00	15·8	2 51	3 40	20 20	21 09
165	14	s	-00 01	-00 07	12 00	15·8	2 51	3 40	20 21	21 10
166	15	Sun	-00 14	-00 20	12 00	15·8	2 51	3 39	20 21	21 10
167	16	M	-00 27	-00 33	12 01	15·8	2 51	3 39	20 22	21 11
168	17	Tu	-00 39	-00 46	12 01	15·8	2 50	3 39	20 22	21 11
169	18	W	-00 53	-00 59	12 01	15·8	2 50	3 39	20 23	21 12
170	19	Th	-01 06	-01 12	12 01	15·8	2 50	3 39	20 23	21 12
171	20	F	-01 19	-01 25	12 01	15·8	2 51	3 39	20 23	21 12
172	21	s	-01 32	-01 38	12 02	15·8	2 51	3 40	20 24	21 13
173	22	Sun	-01 45	-01 51	12 02	15·8	2 51	3 40	20 24	21 13
174	23	M	-01 58	-02 04	12 02	15·8	2 52	3 41	20 24	21 13
175	24	Tu	-02 11	-02 17	12 02	15·8	2 52	3 41	20 24	21 13
176	25	W	-02 24	-02 30	12 02	15·8	2 53	3 41	20 24	21 13
177	26	Th	-02 36	-02 43	12 03	15·8	2 53	3 42	20 24	21 13
178	27	F	-02 49	-02 55	12 03	15·8	2 54	3 42	20 24	21 13
179	28	s	-03 01	-03 07	12 03	15·8	2 54	3 43	20 24	21 12
180	29	Sun	-03 13	-03 19	12 03	15·8	2 55	3 43	20 24	21 12
181	30	M	-03 25	-03 31	12 04	15·8	2 55	3 43	20 23	21 11

G.M.T.

Lat. Corr. to Sunrise, Sunset, etc.

Lat.	Twi-light (h. m.)	Sunrise	Sunset	Twi-light
N70	S.A.H.	S.A.H.	S.A.H.	S.A.H.
68	S.A.H.	S.A.H.	S.A.H.	S.A.H.
66	S.A.H.	S.A.H.	S.A.H.	S.A.H.
64	T.A.N.	-2 06	+2 07	T.A.N.
62	T.A.N.	-1 29	+1 30	+1 58
N60	-1 57	-1 03	+1 04	+1 11
58	-1 09	-0 43	+0 43	+0 40
56	-0 39	-0 26	+0 26	+0 18
54	-0 17	-0 12	+0 12	-0 15
N50	+0 16	+0 11	-0 11	-0 45
45	+0 45	+0 33	-0 34	-1 07
40	+1 07	+0 51	-0 51	-1 25
35	+1 25	+1 06	-1 06	-1 40
30	+1 40	+1 19	-1 20	-2 05
N20	+2 05	+1 41	-1 41	-2 26
N10	+2 26	+2 00	-2 00	-2 44
0	+2 44	+2 18	-2 18	-3 01
S10	+3 01	+2 35	-2 36	-3 18
20	+3 18	+2 54	-2 54	-3 37
30	+3 37	+3 15	-3 15	-3 48
S35	+3 48	+3 27	-3 28	-3 59
40	+3 59	+3 41	-3 42	-4 13
45	+4 13	+3 58	-3 58	-4 29
S50	+4 29	+4 19	-4 19	

NOTES.

Equation of Time is plus until the 14th. When it becomes minus, add to Mean Time. To obtain E, add/subtract Equation of Time to/from 12 hrs. E is always plus (+) to Mean Time. The Lat. Corr. to Sunrise, Sunset, etc., is for the middle of June. S.A.H. means Sun above horizon. T.A.N. means Twilight all night. Examples are given on page 103 onwards.

Table 2

STAR OR PLANET ALTITUDE TOTAL CORRECTION TABLE

ALWAYS SUBTRACTIVE (—)

HEIGHT OF EYE ABOVE THE SEA IN FEET.

Obs. Alt.	5	10	15	20	25	30	35	40	45	50	55	60	70
9°	8·0	8·9	9·6	10·3	10·7	11·2	11·6	12·0	12·4	12·8	13·1	13·5	14·1
10°	7·4	8·4	9·1	9·7	10·2	10·6	11·1	11·5	11·8	12·2	12·5	12·9	13·5
11°	7·0	7·9	8·6	9·2	9·7	10·2	10·6	11·0	11·4	11·8	12·0	12·4	13·0
12°	6·6	7·5	8·2	8·8	9·3	9·8	10·2	10·6	11·0	11·4	11·6	12·0	12·6
13°	6·2	7·2	7·9	8·4	9·0	9·4	9·9	10·3	10·6	11·0	11·3	11·6	12·3
14°	5·9	6·9	7·6	8·1	8·6	9·2	9·6	10·0	10·3	10·7	11·0	11·3	12·0
15°	5·7	6·6	7·3	7·9	8·4	8·9	9·3	9·7	10·1	10·4	10·8	11·1	11·7
16°	5·5	6·4	7·1	7·7	8·2	8·7	9·1	9·5	9·9	10·2	10·5	10·9	11·5
17°	5·3	6·2	6·9	7·5	8·0	8·5	8·9	9·3	9·7	10·0	10·3	10·7	11·3
18°	5·1	6·0	6·7	7·3	7·8	8·3	8·7	9·1	9·5	9·8	10·2	10·5	11·1
19°	4·9	5·8	6·5	7·1	7·6	8·1	8·5	8·9	9·3	9·6	10·0	10·3	11·0
20°	4·8	5·7	6·4	7·0	7·5	8·0	8·4	8·8	9·2	9·6	9·9	10·2	10·8
25°	4·2	5·1	5·8	6·4	6·9	7·4	7·8	8·2	8·6	9·0	9·3	9·6	10·2
30°	3·8	4·7	5·4	6·0	6·5	7·0	7·4	7·8	8·2	8·6	8·9	9·2	9·8
35°	3·5	4·4	5·1	5·7	6·3	6·7	7·2	7·6	7·9	8·3	8·6	8·9	9·5
40°	3·3	4·2	4·9	5·5	6·0	6·5	6·9	7·3	7·7	8·1	8·4	8·7	9·3
50°	3·0	3·9	4·6	5·2	5·7	6·2	6·6	7·0	7·4	7·7	8·1	8·4	9·0
60°	2·7	3·6	4·3	4·9	5·5	5·9	6·4	6·8	7·1	7·5	7·8	8·1	8·8
70°	2·5	3·4	4·1	4·7	5·3	5·7	6·2	6·6	6·9	7·3	7·6	7·9	8·6
80°	2·3	3·3	4·0	4·6	5·1	5·5	6·0	6·4	6·7	7·1	7·4	7·8	8·4
90°	2·2	3·1	3·8	4·4	4·9	5·4	5·8	6·2	6·6	6·9	7·3	7·6	8·2

Tables reproduced by kind permission of Thomas Reed Publications Ltd.

Postscript

This book will give you the bare bones of sextant navigation – you mustn't expect that it'll answer every question, or meet every contingency. I promised you simplicity: I hope you found it simple. Theory was kept to a minimum: I hope you found it practical. It takes nerve to sail over the rim of the horizon for the first time, but I hope this book will help you to make the break. Choose the day with care: get well off the shore and start practising with the sextant – it's easier than you think!

ANSWERS TO PROBLEMS

Chapter Six (page 53)
1. Time – 12.28.20 GMT   Latitude – 51° 08.9′ N
2. Time – 12.47.00 BST   Latitude – 54° 25.3′ N
3. Time – 12.33.20 GMT   Latitude – 47° 27.4′ N

Chapter Seven (page 60)
1. Latitude – 49° 56.6′ N

Chapter Nine (page 74)
Azimuth – 088°T
Intercept – 4.7′ 'away'

Glossary

Aries,
first point of . . .
Also known as the Vernal (Spring) Equinox, it is the point where the sun crosses the celestial equator and changes its declination from South to North.

Calculated
zenith distance
The theoretical distance from the dead reckoning to the geographical position.

Celestial sphere
The dome of the heavens on which the planets and stars appear to be placed in the night sky.

Centring error
An error of the sextant caused by the index bar not pivoting exactly at the centre of the arc.

Collimation
error
Exists in sextants where the optical axis of the telescope is not parallel with the plane of the instrument.

Declination
The angular distance of a heavenly body north or south of the celestial equator.

Departure
The distance covered in nautical miles east or west when a ship is sailing from one place to another along a rhumb line.

Difference
of latitude
The difference of latitude between two places on the surface of the earth is the arc of a meridian between the parallels of latitude where the places are situated.

Difference
of longitude
The arc of the equator between the meridians where two places are situated: it is found by adding the two longitudes together when they are of opposite name, or by subtracting the smaller from the greater when they are of the same name.

Dip
The angle between the horizontal plane through the eye of the observer and the apparent plane of the visible horizon.

Equator
A great circle round the earth, every part of which is equidistant from the Poles.

Estimated
position
The best estimate you can make of your position taking all relevant factors into consideration.

Geographical position	A point on the earth's surface where an imaginary line from the centre of a heavenly body to the centre of the earth passes through the earth's crust.
Gnomonic projection	A form of chart construction where great circles appear as straight lines.
Great circle	A circle whose plane passes through the centre of a sphere dividing it into two equal halves.
Greenwich hour angle	The angle at the Pole measured westwards from the Greenwich meridian to the meridian passing through a geographical position.
Index error	A common sextant error due to small differences between the sextant angle and the scale reading.
Intercept	The difference between the observed zenith distance and the calculated zenith distance.
Latitude	The angular distance of a point on the surface of the earth measured north or south of the equator.
Local hour angle	The angular distance from the longitude of the observer measured westwards to the longitude of the geographical position of a heavenly body.
Longitude	The smaller angle at the Pole between the meridian of Greenwich and the meridian of a position on the surface of the earth measured east or west of Greenwich.
Mercator's projection	A form of chart construction with the meridians drawn parallel to each other so that a rhumb line cuts each meridian at the same angle.
Meridian altitude	The highest point reached by a heavenly body each day.
Observed zenith distance	The distance from the geographical position to the position line. It is compared with the calculated zenith distance to obtain the intercept.
Parallax	Parallax exists because observations are taken from the surface of the earth and not at its centre. The small correction required is usually included in a total correction table.

Perpendicularity	An error of the sextant caused by the index mirror not being perpendicular to the plane of the instrument.
Refraction	Refraction arises from the bending of light rays when they pass through the earth's atmosphere. It is usually allowed for in a total correction table.
Rhumb line	A line on the surface of the earth that cuts all meridians at the same angle.
Semi-diameter	The altitude of a heavenly body is usually measured by reference to the lower limb if it is reasonably large. Semi-diameter is the correction necessary to relate the reading to the centre of the body.
Side error	A sextant error arising when the horizon mirror is not perpendicular with the plane of the instrument.
Sidereal hour angle	The SHA of a star is the angle measured westerly at the Pole between the meridian of Aries and the meridian of the star.
Zenith	When a body is directly overhead from an observer it is said to be in his zenith.